Thomson's Pulp Mill:

Building the Champion Fibre Company at Canton, North Carolina 1905 to 1908

Carroll C. Jones

Jan-Carol
Publishing, Inc
"every story needs a book"

Thomson's Pulp Mill:
Building the Champion Fibre Company
at Canton, North Carolina
1905 to 1908

Carroll C. Jones

Published August 2018
Little Creek Books
Imprint of Jan-Carol Publishing, Inc
All rights reserved
Copyright © 2018 by Carroll C. Jones
Book Design by Brandon Goins

ISBN: 978-1-945619-67-0
Library of Congress Control Number: 2018952821

You may contact the publisher:
Jan-Carol Publishing, Inc
PO Box 701
Johnson City, TN 37605
publisher@jancarolpublishing.com
jancarolpublishing.com

This book is dedicated to the memory of my father, Albert Carroll (Tony) Jones,
who worked tirelessly during his lifetime for the benefit of his family,
the community, and the Canton paper mill.

CONTENTS

DEAR READER

I cannot describe to you the feeling of fulfill-ment that has come over me while working on this latest writing project. Most readers will be unaware that my professional career began as a young engineer at Champion International's paper mill in Canton, North Carolina. Certainly, I knew the plant had been around for a long time. After all, I was born and raised in Canton and my great grandfather, a Civil War veteran, helped build the mill in the early 1900's.

Still, I was surprised to discover original brick construction, timber post and beam framing, and steam engines while prowling the darkest corners of the seventy-year-old mill during those first years of my employ-ment. Being a history lover, I was simply enthralled with these leftover elements of the early Champion Fibre Company factory.

A couple of years ago, I stumbled upon a rare trove of old photographs made during the period when the original Champion Fibre

pulp mill and extract plant were under construction—between 1905 and 1908. Upon seeing them, old memories were stoked and that innate affinity for history I have always carried became too hot to quench. So I decided to use these wonderful pictures to tell the story of the mammoth pulp mill Peter Gibson Thomson built on the bank of the Pigeon River.

Of course there are many former and cur-rent employees who are extremely familiar with the more recent pulp and paper-manu-facturing operations and updated facilities. However, even if you fall into that category you might be clueless—just like I was—as to why and how the original pulp mill and tan-nin extract plant were built in, of all places, the little town of Canton. And I have an idea that most folks will be in that same boat. So, please, find a comfy chair, sit back, and enjoy this trip back in time.

Best regards,
Carroll C. Jones

ACKNOWLEDGEMENTS

Most of the wonderful photographs presented in this book were made between 1905 and 1908, showing the original Champion Fibre Company pulp mill and tannin extract plant being constructed in Canton, North Carolina. Journalists and an incredulous public referred to the mammoth mill as "Thomson's pulp mill," after Peter Gibson Thomson who was erecting the towering brick buildings. For more than a century now, many of these photos of the construction work have been carefully packed away in drawers and closets, and only pulled out for viewing on very special occasions. One can imagine them being shared with guests gathered and chatting around the dining table, radio, or television set, and being viewed in wonder and appreciation.

Thomas Marr, especially, would have had a lot to allow about them, given the important role he played in the construction of Peter Thomson's pulp mill. Mr. Marr was in charge of building the employee village known as "Fibreville" and the mill's large tannin extract plant, which he would later superintend. Over the many years since the photographs were taken, they have been proudly passed down from Marr to his niece and her husband, the late Mary and Howard Sellars, and then on to their sons, Alan and Steve Sellars. It is because of these brothers' wishes for the photographs to be seen and appreciated that they can be presented in this book. I am very grateful for

their generosity, as I am sure you will be.

Every week or so there are a few history lovers who gather around a table at the Canton Area Historical Museum. There, they visit and talk about such things as the history of Canton, the latest donation to the museum, a new discovery made by the museum's capable curator, ways to enhance the interpretive exhibits, or an old photo that has been enhanced, enlarged, and printed for everyone's enjoyment. These "friends of the museum" were kind enough to welcome me into their group and share an extensive knowledge of our home town. Discussions of the "Rooshians" building the original Champion Fibre Company's mill, the origins of Canton's old iron-truss bridge, the location of Penland's fording spot at the village of Pigeon River, and many other fascinating topics revived fond memories and a love for my home town that I had never lost—even after an absence of almost thirty-five years.

It was through these friends that I first became aware of two men's spiral-bound, type-written memoirs held in the museum. The authors who penned these memories were Reuben B. Robertson, Sr., the long-time leader of the Champion Fibre Company and later the Champion Paper and Fibre Company, and George H. Smathers, an attorney for the Company in the first decades of its existence. Mostly unedited and full of typographical issues, as well as missing pages, the memoirs relate stories tied to the founding and early history of the Champion Fibre Company. I have made liberal use of these rich documents in telling the story of the construction of Thomson's pulp mill. Certainly, memories can sometimes be faulty, no matter who is doing the remembering. They can also change with time as we gray and slow down, sounding better and better as embellishments are woven into favorite tales. Clearly, Mr. Robertson's and Mr. Smathers' memoirs have been utilized in a manner that recognizes these tendencies that can befall us all.

Another very valuable source of information that has added to our knowledge of the construction of Thomson's pulp mill are the "clippings" extracted from century-old newspaper editions found online. Through these contemporaneous reports, I learned how the construction of the "mammoth Thomson's pulp mill" was hyped to a dubious public. Western North Carolinians read about an outlander from Ohio named Peter G. Thomson who had the gumption to up and build an enormous plant for producing wood pulp and tannin extract—right in their neck of the woods. Of course most of them had never heard of such a thing, and could not get enough "news" to satisfy their keen curiosities. The *Asheville Citizen-Times*, *Charlotte Observer*, *The News and Observer* published in Raleigh, and many other papers were inclined to print whatever news about Thomson's pulp mill their wandering journalists could uncover or that "a gentleman passing through and in the know"

might have revealed. Also, it was through these same primary sources that details of horrific accidents frequently came to light during the construction period. News of a man falling to his death or being crushed by a tumbling brick wall became standard fare. After awhile, gruesome reports like these failed to raise the eyebrows of mountaineers reading their favorite paper.

I am extremely grateful to the current leaders of Evergreen Packaging Company's Canton Mill for granting me access to their facility and allowing me to rummage through old stomping grounds in the engineering offices. Several hours of searching turned up one drawing by the original architect of the mill, George F. Hardy of New York City. This old engineering document, although badly faded, revealed the foundation plans for the pulp mill (but not the tannin extract plant) and proved to be very enlightening. It provided the layout and sizes of many buildings, clues to the different processes housed inside them, and, importantly, details of the extensive timber piling that was driven into the ground to support the massive brick buildings and machinery.

A few history-loving individuals have been kind enough to read versions of my manuscript and offer encouraging and constructive comments. Included among these bright-minded literary critics were Edie Hutchins Burnette, Camille Wells, Phil Paxton, Bill Rolland, and Evelyn Coltman. I appreciate the valuable time that each and every one of them dedicated to this project. Thank you!

Camille Wells' special literary skills and expertise in architectural history enabled her to suggest ways to enhance the Champion Fibre construction story. I am grateful for the untold hours she spent reading and editing to make this book as accurate and complete as possible. The information contained in Camille's own important book, *Canton: The Architecture of Our Home Town*, has proved invaluable to me in many instances. I have always admired this early work of hers and am pleased to report that the book is still in print and available at the Canton Area Historical Museum. Camille was even willing to contribute the Foreword for *Thomson's Pulp Mill*, and I can think of no one more respected or qualified to write it.

Two gentlemen whose great-grandparents were crucially linked to the Champion Fibre Company story shared some personal insight with me. Peter Robinson very willingly talked about several aspects of his Great-Grandfather Peter G. Thomson's early life and professional career. And well-known local attorney, Roy Patton, offered thoughts on the intriguing story of his Great-Grandmother Mary Ann Patton's real estate dealings with Peter Thomson and Attorney George H. Smathers. By the way, this is the same Mrs. Patton that Thomson claimed was "one of the smartest women he had ever talked to."

Many others provided information, stories, and support as I endeavored to uncover the history of Thomson's pulp mill. Case in point, Patsy and Dan Kelly related for my benefit their memories of the Canton mill. In our conversation, I learned that one of Dan's important tasks as a young electrician in the mill had been to walk over to Fibreville, every now and again, and replace burned-out light bulbs in the company's employee houses. Later in his career, though, Dan worked in the purchasing department. One particular project that he remembered was the demolition of the flared top on the great concrete smokestack that has loomed over Canton for more than a century. It turns out, that while I was in Brazil in the early 1980's working for Champion International, the 250-feet high chimney constructed in 1907 was diminished by fifty feet. As this book goes to press, the Evergreen Packaging Company is in the process of completing the demolition work. By the end of 2018 the huge monolith will be forever erased from Canton's topography, with only memories and old photographs to show for it.

At the Haywood Community College, Hilary Cobb provided able and professional assistance in developing a plot plan—or footprint—of Thomson's pulp mill and tannin extract facilities. This drawing and its corresponding legend should prove to be extremely helpful in orienting readers with the layout and identity of the various brick buildings that comprised the original mill.

Caroline Ponton, curator at the Canton Area Historical Museum, has offered her tireless assistance in finding appropriate source material and photos from the Canton Area Historical Museum's bounty of his-

xii

torical documents. Also, Roland Osborne, whose knowledge of Canton, its history, and its citizenry is truly extraordinary, used his photography skills to scan, enhance, and reproduce various old photographs that are presented in this book. I am truly grateful to both of them for the time, expertise, and generous help they have provided.

It is my good fortune to have a publisher who recognizes the significance of the material presented in this book. Jan-Carol Publishing's team has done an excellent job with the book design. Let me offer a special

thanks to Brandon Goins, who had the patience to work closely with this engineer to get everything just right.

Lastly, let me say that it really feels good to be home again, from time to time, and rooting around to uncover the history of my home town. I want to thank all of the citizens of Canton and employees of the mill, past and present, for contributing to the many fond memories that I harbor. Please consider this book, *Thomson's Pulp Mill*, as a token of my appreciation.

FOREWORD

By Camille Wells

Every place has a past—that is, whatever happened before what we know as "now." During the past two or three generations, those of us who grew up in Canton, North Carolina heard from our elders something about the coming of Champion's paper mill, even though its vast and ominous presence made it seem truly permanent and immutable—like gravity. But the mill <u>came</u> to Canton, and that means there was a time before its arrival when this place had very different characteristics. As far back as the Civil War era, a graded turnpike connecting Asheville with east Tennessee coursed through the Pigeon River Valley, traversing the river where it was wide and shallow enough for animals and wagons to cross in safety. All around this inviting intersection of road and flowing water at Ford of the Pigeon, buildings for various purposes began to cluster. In 1882, a railroad providing more efficient access to the east changed the scale but not the character of life in this useful little village. Then comes a lapse, an elision in this history of place...

When I was growing up, our neighbor William "Billy" Battison often crossed Hampton Heights during summer evenings to visit my family and share watermelon in our back yard. When he came, I usually stopped playing with my brother and our friends so I could hear what he had to say. Among the many vanished sights

and events he conjured was how builders of the mill worked so hard to set wooden "pilings" below the foundations of each structure. With a child's mind, I pictured the heavy timbers of which he spoke as laying out flat on the ground, side by side. I would not have thought they were set vertically, one on top of the other, and driven impossibly deep into the ground. I was lucky to have Mr. Battison for a neighbor and I wish I remembered more of what he said, for he was actually closing a gap in the town's knowledge of itself—not in mine. Throughout the span of living memory, most Canton residents have told children and visitors <u>when</u> the mill came to Canton, but not <u>how</u>. It may as well have arrived like one of those "Modern Homes" that Sears, Roebuck and Company began to sell in 1908: on a train in tidy, ready-to-assemble pieces accompanied by detailed diagrams and printed instructions.

The coming of the mill to Canton was not nearly as tidy as that. Before it was constructed there, the mountain people of North Carolina knew very little of mechanized production. The knowledge they possessed was primarily limited to the blacksmiths' shops and the machinery and processes encountered at gristmills, where their grain crops were rendered into meal and flour. After all, theirs was an age-old agrarian economy based on fairly traditional methods for meeting their needs. Between plantings and harvestings, farmers would eventually adopt an off-season strategy to enhance their income—felling logs to transport and sell. In the decades following the Civil War, railroad companies began clearing roadbeds and laying wooden crossties under steel rails beyond the farmers immediate horizons. With each year that passed, these ribbons of steel reached ever farther into the state and up the easternmost slopes of the mountains.

The major railroads could reach only so far into mountainous timberland, and the logging industry that sprouted along the tracks harvested the largest and oldest hardwoods the farmers and loggers could find, fell, and drag to the mills or the trains. In a second phase of timbering, the companies built narrow-gauge rail lines along steeper grades leading farther into the woods. They also began establishing timber camps where loggers could live close to their freshest job sites. Originally envisioned as entirely transitory, a number of these camps grew to considerable size with amenities for families as well as workmen: reasonably comfortable housing, fencing for yards and gardens, commissaries, churches that doubled as schools, and halls set up for musical performances, dances, and other forms of recreation. These busy settlements had names like Oakmont, Crestmont, Ravensford, Smokemont, Robbinsville, and Sunburst.

By the 1920's, profits from industrialized lumbering had dwindled to an extent that motivated most of the lumber companies to leave the mountains for more promising wooded terrain. One northern capitalist

who had no intention of departing was Peter G. Thomson. The wealth that financed his ventures in western North Carolina came from the production of coated paper at the thriving factory he had built in Hamilton, Ohio. But the wood pulp from which his valuable paper products were manufactured was becoming more and more difficult to acquire. It was this critical resource—wood—that drove Thomson, like the lumber companies, to buy hundreds of thousands of acres of southern mountain timberland. While Thomson certainly regarded the lumbering business as essentially extractive, he meant to log selectively, felling only the species that produced the best pulp. Furthermore, he intended to transport those logs no farther than the pulp mill he planned to build in Canton, on the banks of the Pigeon River.

So clear-cutting did not serve his interests, nor did only short-term employment for the mountain loggers serve his purposes. Thomson's intended investment in the mountains of western North Carolina was too deeply rooted and, potentially, sustainably profitable. Unlike all his counterparts, he saw in western North Carolina not only the timber he needed, but also minimal competition for the other valuable resources he required: access to freight transport by rail, access to an abundant water supply from the Pigeon River, and access to a plentiful native labor force accustomed to the arduous tasks of working a mountain farm. These mountain men were willing to build Thomson's pulp mill in Canton, and he calculated they would be willing to keep it generating a pulp supply for his coated paper mill in Ohio.

The gift that Carroll Jones—engineer, writer, historian, and Canton native—has bestowed in his *Thomson's Pulp Mill* is the wondrous story of a mammoth pulp mill's construction at Canton. At the outset, Jones introduces and brings startlingly to life the prosperous yet unprepossessing little town before he plunges it into a fascinating crucible of enormous disruption, confusion, and reorientation. Newcomers—foreign workmen and city men with unfamiliar technologies and styles of organization, not to mention very different ideas about work and production—completely transformed the population, scale, and purpose of the town. From this ordeal, Champion Fibre Company was born, emerging as the huge, loud, and strenuously efficient factory that Peter Thomson envisioned.

In addition to his talents in research and writing, Jones brings to this subject his life's work: his profession as an engineer who specialized in the construction, modification, and operation of modern paper mills. He has assembled the evidence for us and interpreted it with such expertise that we can understand how a mill of a much earlier generation was erected, equipped with all the proper machinery, and then set in motion. The significance of Thomson's decision to locate his pulp mill in Canton, North Carolina is almost impossible to exaggerate, and Carroll Jones shows how and why it occurred. He has recovered from astonishing obscurity a crucial series of events in Canton's past. Through his exceptional talents and relentless pursuit of the actual story behind Thomson's pulp mill, he has turned this past into a history.

Camille Wells, author of *Material Witnesses*, has taught early American history, architectural history, historic preservation, and material culture at the University of Mary Washington, the University of Virginia School of Architecture, and the College of William and Mary.

PREFACE

Thomson's Pulp Mill offers a concise and illustrated account of the construction of Peter Gibson Thomson's pulp mill in Canton, North Carolina, more than a century ago. Originally known as the Champion Fibre Company, it later evolved into the Champion Paper and Fibre Company and several other concerns through the years. Not only will the reader discover a very practical reason that drove Mr. Thomson to build the mill, but also why the tiny town of Canton was chosen as its location, what that original mill entailed, and how tremendous challenges were overcome to construct the immense brick buildings. More importantly, many wonderful and rare old photographs that have come to light are presented in this book. These serve to illuminate the construction project from the driving of the first timber piles into the muddy bottomland to the spewing of smoke from the mill's signature towering chimney.

Fresh out of college, I went to work for Champion International as an engineer, unaware of the wetness that still dripped from behind my ears. Thank goodness there were experienced co-workers in the Canton paper mill's engineering department who covered for me, while I became accustomed to designing and building projects—first small maintenance jobs and, gradually, larger and more sophisticated projects. During that initial year or so, I was able to explore every dark corner of the mill's vast facilities, trying to figure out how things were built, how they worked, and,

most of all, where I was. Those first impressions of timber framing, brick masonry constructions, and an ancient steam engine driving a paper machine with pulleys and leather belts remained with me through the coming decades while I worked in the paper industry.

Lately, a good portion of my time has been dedicated to either historical writing projects or to fly fishing. In pursuit of knowledge and local history—not the local wild trout—it has been my pleasure and good fortune to become acquainted with the important resources held at the Canton Area Historical Museum. These holdings, along with lively conversations with the museum's curator and friends of the museum, have served to revive nearly forgotten memories of the Canton paper mill. I discovered in the museum unpublished memoirs of two principal men in the history of the Champion Fibre Company: Reuben B. Robertson, Sr., who for many years helmed the mill operations and later the affairs of the entire company, and attorney George H. Smathers, who played an instrumental legal role in the development of the original pulp mill.

These men's documented memories—such as the one of the "Rooshians" (the name given by locals to the foreign workmen from Bulgaria) and another about the attempts, through hypnosis, to persuade a local widow lady to sell her land to the Champion Fibre Company—kindled my desire to write about the construction of the original mill. However, even these rich typewritten memoirs did not provide enough source material to record the true construction story. So, I abandoned that thought as a mere fancy and one that could never come to fruition. There simply was not enough extant information to do a proper job—I thought.

Then one day, I ran into an old high school friend for the first time in many years. He was a Canton boy and, like me, had spent most of his professional career away from our home town. As we caught up and resumed our acquaintance, he offhandedly mentioned some old mill construction photos in his possession. Well, as it happens, his late mother's Uncle Thomas Marr played a vital role in the construction of the original mill's tannin extract plant and the employee village known as "Fibreville." Later, Mr. Marr became the superintendent in charge of the entire extract department, which was a highly profitable operation for the Champion Fibre Company, even carrying the company through some problematic growing times. These old photographs of the construction work had been passed down through Mr. Marr's family, ending up in the appreciative hands of my friend.

One look at this immense trove of rare photos convinced me that they should be preserved and shared somehow. Admittedly, the quality of some of the images is poor but, even so, they offer a glimpse into the obscure past and show the pulp mill under construction—a sight almost lost to us forever. The notion of presenting the photographs in a book format so that they could be interpreted, understood, and appreciated became too strong to ignore. My friend agreed with the idea and has very graciously allowed them to be included in *Thomson's Pulp Mill*. Therefore,

I have endeavored to associate these photographs with a narrative story about the construction of the Champion Fibre Company mill at Canton. Detailed captions accompany most of the photos, offering as much insight as I have been able to glean and understand. There are also a few other photographs from the Canton Area Historical Museum's collection that have been used to supplement the visual treasures contained within this book.

It will become obvious to the reader where the source material for the story comes from. Footnotes and the bibliography will show that most of the historical information is derived from either the Robertson and Smathers memoirs or newspaper articles published at the time of the mill's construction. In every case, I tried to find more than one newspaper account to authenticate some of the reported facts. For those who might wonder, many instances of inaccurate reporting (or "fake news") indeed came to light.

Likewise, I did not take the memoirs at face value. Both men recorded their memories many years after the fact. Mr. Robertson even wrote in a foreword to his memoirs that since "none of those who carried responsibility in Champion's infancy are with us today...one's style is not therefore in any way cramped by the fear of the carping criticism of those who might want meticulous accuracy."[1] Due consideration was given to these words as I crafted *Thomson's Pulp Mill*, using the "facts," stories, and tales from the Robertson and Smathers memoirs. Where deemed necessary, readers are reminded that these were the men's recollections, and memories are not infallible.

However, as you will discover, these dated type-written memoirs are rich beyond description, providing us invaluable information as well as interesting tales of the history of Thomson's pulp mill.

Actual details of the original mill and machinery are exceedingly scarce. A foundation plan drawn by George F. Hardy, the mill's architect/engineer, was discovered in the archives of the Evergreen Packaging Company's Canton mill. This document provided the foundation details of the pulp mill, but excluded the extract plant structures, two other large wood preparation buildings, the river pump house, and a water reservoir situated high on a hill above the mill. Although the poor condition of this old print made it barely decipherable, it proved extremely helpful in determining the layout and size of many of the original buildings. Not only that, it showed the piling details under each building, so that the true scope of the piling work can be fully understood and appreciated.

For example, various reports at the time of the construction work stated that the mill's huge concrete smokestack was built on top of either four hundred timber piles or a thousand piles, depending on the source of information. However, both of these counts can be disputed with confidence, since the Hardy drawing very specifically shows that approximately two hundred piles were actually used.

An edition of *Manufacturer's Record* published at the time of construction contains a very descriptive article of Thomson's enterprise, including details of the mill's various buildings and some of the mechanical equipment housed within the brick walls. Yet, much is not known about many of the specific machines employed in the mill—their make, size, and how they functioned and were operated. Nevertheless, I describe the original mill's pulping and extract processes in sufficient detail to satisfy most readers' appetites for such things. Also, a listing of all the different buildings, along with the size and contents of each one, is included. And to better orient readers with these facilities, a plot plan of the mill buildings is presented as well.

This story and the descriptions of the original Champion Fibre Company mill are surely important, and undoubtedly readers will find the information interesting and enlightening. But it is the rare old photographs that demonstrate in magnificent detail how the mill site looked just prior to construction, during the construction period in 1906 and 1907, and after the 1908 start-up. Only to the discerning eye will the challenging conditions that the men worked in, the sheer massiveness of the structures and equipment they erected, and much more be comprehended.

It will be my great privilege now to escort you back into a mill town's past, where the story of Thomson's pulp mill will be revealed at last.

Peter Gibson Thomson was the founder and president of the Champion Coated Paper Company in Hamilton, Ohio. In 1905, he made his first exploratory trips into western North Carolina in search of a pulp mill site. (from Canton Area Historical Museum)

Chapter 1
Site Selection

Just after the turn of the twentieth century, profits at the Champion Coated Paper Company based in Hamilton, Ohio were soaring and President Peter G. Thomson wanted more. The far-sighted businessman, who had started out as a bookstore owner and printer, decided to modernize and expand his paper-coating enterprise on the bank of the Great Miami River, twenty miles north of Cincinnati. In 1902, four new paper machines were purchased and installed, allowing Thomson to control the supply and price of the paper to be coated through the company's proprietary double-coating process.

One of the most skilled papermakers in the industry was recruited from the Oxford Paper Company to manage the new paper production operation. His name was Jim Harris, and it was not long before the redheaded Irishman began pressuring his new boss to fully integrate their process.[2] At the time, the Hamilton mill was purchasing wood pulp on the open market and using it to manufacture paper and coated products. Harris promoted the benefits of producing their own pulp in order to control the supply and price of this primary raw material. More importantly, however, was something dearer to his boss's heart. Harris was adamant in asserting that a good quality paper could only be produced from high-quality pulp. Eventually, Peter Thomson came around, and by early 1905 he was looking in earnest for a suitable place to manufacture wood pulp.[3]

Past vacations to the Blue Ridge Mountains and memories of train trips to Asheville, North Carolina, where his son, Logan, had boarded and studied at the Asheville School, surely influenced Peter Thomson's decision to search the virgin forests of western North Carolina. Early exploratory excursions revealed that vast quantities of spruce timber abounded along some of the region's high crests. This was the specific species needed to support the sulphite-pulping process, which was the predominant chemical method for rendering high-quality, "long-fiber" pulp from spruce wood chips. At the lower elevations, entire mountainsides were covered with towering stands of hardwoods, including huge chestnut trees. Thomson was keenly aware that tannin acids could be extracted from chestnut wood and sold profitably to the leather tanning industry. Certainly, the Carolina highlands abounded in the wood he sought, but where in this backwoods country could a modern mill be built to convert the valuable resource into pulp?

Very early in 1905, a meeting was held at the Dickey boarding house in the little railroad town of Murphy to discuss the matter of timberlands and possible sites for Thomson's pulp mill. John Q. Barker had invited Peter Thomson and more than twenty local businessmen to that remote place in Cherokee County, situated at the southwestern tip of North Carolina. Barker, a lumber and tannin extract man, and the others were anxious to promote the region's timber resources and their own interests. At the outset, Thomson stated that the primary purpose of his visit was to select a site where he could build a pulp mill—one that had an abundant supply of water and access to pulp woods within a hundred-mile radius that could supply the plant for twenty-five years.[4] Much discussion ensued and exploratory trips to various woodland tracts were contemplated, including one to the Three M Lumber Company camp located at Smokemont in Swain County. It was at this place that Thomson first met Samuel Montgomery Smith.

About fifty-years old at the time, Mr. Smith was tall, raw-boned, and weighed around two-hundred pounds. Described as being perfectly erect and as stolid in appearance as an Indian, his brilliant blue eyes never wavered from the face of the man to whom he was talking. Smith probably knew more about the different timber tracts in western North Carolina than any other man alive. At Smokemont, the woodsman informed Thomson of a large quantity of spruce and hardwood timber held by several entities in Haywood County, including the Haywood Lumber and Mining Company and Cornelius W. Amsler and Associates. So impressed was Thomson with the prospects of this bounty that he was moved to see it for himself, and he persuaded Montgomery Smith to accompany him to these pristine forests located on the headwaters of Haywood County's Pigeon River.[5, 6]

It is hard to imagine the wealthy capitalist Thomson, who was fifty-four years old at the time, trekking along with Montgomery Smith into the furthest reaches of the Pigeon River tributaries and scaling the surrounding high mountains—but that is just what he did. During that first scouting trip, Smith likely began agitating Thomson with the thought of building a log flume from the Pigeon lands all the way to Canton, a small town located some sixteen to eighteen miles downstream and situated alongside the Pigeon River and the Murphy Branch of the Southern Railway Company.

The merits of the idea, as Smith saw them, were that all of the lumber needed to construct the flume and support the construction of the plant could be sawn at the Pigeon

Attorney George H. Smathers worked tirelessly for Peter G. Thomson in the early days of the Champion Fibre Company. He was tasked with securing land titles and rights-of-way and doing other important legal work to get the enterprise started. (from NCpedia website)

headlands and sluiced down the river to the construction site in Canton at a very low cost. Additionally, after the mill was up and running, the pulpwood could be got out, sawn into the proper size, and conveyed down the flume to the mill, again at a low cost. It was surely an enticing idea, this flume scheme, and one that eventually caused Thomson to become somewhat partial to building his mill at Canton.

While standing atop a high point known as Shining Rock, within full view of magnificent spruce stands along the high mountain ridges and dense hardwood forests beneath them, Peter Thomson engaged the services of the able woodsman. Smith agreed to a salary of two hundred dollars a month to assist Thomson in the search for the best possible mill site.

Afterward, the two men travelled down to Canton to assess the situation there, such as the railroad infrastructure, availability of land along the railroad and against the Pigeon River, the water flow, backup electrical power possibilities, constructability issues, and other things. While still in Haywood County, Thomson hired a lawyer from the county seat town of Waynesville to work with him and Smith in their efforts to get things going. George Henry Smathers was the attorney's name. Apparently he had made quite an impression on Peter Thomson at the Dickey house conference held in Murphy earlier that year. Smathers was highly accomplished in land title work. Among other related land acquisition and legal activities, he had previously helped western North Carolina's

Cherokee people remove trespassers and clear up many land title suits pending against them. Also, he had served as Waynesville's mayor for two terms and as a state senator during the 1897 term. The man was eminently suited to assist Thomson in acquiring the Pigeon timberlands, properties for the mill, and rights-of-way for a flume.

George Smathers later recorded that Peter Thomson held to three requirements that governed whether they should build the mill at Canton. These were as follows:

1) Must be able to purchase at a reasonable price the land on which a pulp mill can be built and operated and houses for the mill's employees can be constructed.

2) Must be able to purchase at a reasonable price the 40,000 acres of timberlands at the headwaters of the east and west forks of the Pigeon River held by several entities. This would be the reserve supply of pulp wood in the event sufficient quantities could not be obtained on the general market.

3) Must be able to secure a contract with the Southern Railway Company for reasonable shipping rates for all the material used in the operation of the plant and for shipping the pulp product to Cincinnati.

In the spring of 1905, all three men—Thomson, Smith, and Smathers—were working towards their common goal of obtaining a site for Thomson's pulp mill.[7] Their first step was to secure the 40,000 acres at the Pigeon River headlands. Negotiations were

undertaken with Thomas Crary, President of the Haywood Lumber and Mining Company, to purchase what was then known as the Crary and Young Pigeon Lands.[8] Thomson offered ten dollars per acre to Crary for 25,000 acres located at the headwaters of the West Fork of the Pigeon River. Thereafter ensued months of protracted and headstrong back-and-forth correspondence, several meetings, threatened law suits, demands, and venting of injured feelings. Finally, in October of 1905, the parties came to terms and Peter Thomson acquired the timberland to support the pulp mill he aimed to build.

During this same time period, Montgomery Smith had been working to secure options for additional tracts at the Pigeon headlands, including a 7,000-acre boundary owned by Cornelius Amsler of Butler, Pennsylvania, some 4,000 acres of Welch and Osborne lands, and another 4,000 acres owned by others. By early 1906, the titles of all these lands along with the Crary-Young tract—40,000 acres in all—were in the name of Peter Thomson.

Additionally, Smith had been able to purchase a piece of land from Mark and Jeremiah Reece in the Three Forks area, where he intended to build a sawmill. By late 1905 or early 1906, Smith had moved his family to Three Forks at Thomson's behest. At that location, where the Middle Prong and Right-Hand Prong tributaries flowed into the West Fork of the Pigeon River, he installed a circular sawmill and shingle machine and promptly began establishing a woods operation. In association with this new lumber enterprise, he was also obliged to construct the quarters and other infrastructure necessary to sustain the loggers, mill workers, and their families in the very remote wilderness setting. A commissary and another two-story building topped by a high belfry were erected. The latter provided an excellent venue for schooling children as well as for meetings of every description, including worshipping and dancing. Very soon, a small village was born at the Three Forks—one which Peter Thomson was moved to name "Sunburst," for the way the morning sun burst over the eastern ridges.[9]

The next Thomson requirement that had to be satisfied before his pulp mill could be established in Canton was to find sufficient land to build on. It had to be next to the river, have railroad access, and, importantly, be procured at a reasonable price. Although the railroad had reached this fording spot on the Pigeon River in 1882, the Town of Canton was still no more than a railroad stop with a conglomeration of frame and tent store buildings, a couple of blacksmith shops, a livery, grist mill, hotel, boarding house, and several churches. When it rained, the unpaved streets became mired in mud, and there were no sidewalks to relieve the pedestrians' woes. As one visitor observed, most of the few hundred citizens were devoted to strict temperance behavior, in regards to consumption of ardent spirits. He described the locals as "being sociable and pleasant, but are of a decidedly religious turn of mind—they won't let you fish on Sunday and frown upon the young folks who are bold enough to buggy ride on the Lord's day."[10]

God-fearing ardor was not uppermost on Peter Thomson's agenda when he first met with the upstanding leaders of Canton in early 1905. His intent was to introduce himself and let it be known that he was considering the construction of a pulp mill in their town. Most of the men were highly pleased with the idea, realizing that other places in western North Carolina were eagerly bidding for Thomson's mill at the time. Not surprisingly, they offered the Ohio businessman their hearty support, including a willingness to deliver substantial tax breaks for the enterprise. It was agreed that they would aid Thomson in finding the necessary land—fairly priced—to build his enormous plant and suitable quarters for the workers to live in.

Among the most cooperative and active of those in attendance at this first meeting were the merchants W.J. (Dick) Hampton, his son-in-law Turner Sharp, Joseph Nelson (Nelse) Mease, Parker McGee, and John W. Scott. Before the meeting adjourned, Thomson gave these five men—whom he later referred to as the "Big Five"—and the others assembled with him something else to think about. He promised them he would not initially open a commissary for some time if they carried out in good faith their unofficial promises. Thereby, the town's merchants would be free to compete for his employees' trade. It was surely an incentive worth thinking about and one enthusiastically received by the Big Five.[11]

This is the small sawmill village of Sunburst, built by Peter G. Thomson and Samuel Montgomery Smith at Three Forks in late 1905 and 1906. Eli Potter is credited with designing the two-story school/church building with the wonderful belfry, which was constructed in only two-weeks time. Prior to joining Champion Fibre Company, Potter worked as a woodsman at George Vanderbilt's Biltmore Estate with Frederick Law Olmsted, Gifford Pinchot, and Dr. Carl Alwin Schenck.

In 1911, after the pulp mill at Canton was fully operational, ownership of the timberlands on the Pigeon River headwaters and the Pigeon River Railway was transferred to the Champion Lumber Company. A new sawmill was built a few miles downstream on the West Fork of the Pigeon River, and the village of Sunburst was relocated there—taking its name with it. Thereafter, the original settlement at Sunburst became known as "Spruce." Spruce's population dwindled over the coming years, although it later hosted a Civilian Conservation Corps camp in the 1930's. (from Canton Area Historical Museum)

Most everyone in western North Carolina was alerted to rumors that a mammoth pulp mill was going to be built somewhere in the mountains. Although Canton seemed to be the front runner, other communities were actively bidding for Thomson's enterprise. Waynesville, Clyde, Sylva, Bryson City, Andrews, Murphy, Asheville, and even Newport, Tennessee were among the places where town fathers' hopes were high that Peter Thomson would look with favor on their communities. An article posted in an Asheville paper revealed one local lawyer's fervent hopes of securing Thomson's pulp mill for that place. "When one considers the immense advantages to be gained by the addition of 1,000 workmen to our city population, it would seem that no stone should be left unturned to secure the plum which threatens to drop. I don't want to wish Canton any bad luck, but that particular spot can't outdo Asheville when it comes to facilities for factories."[12]

Another example of the importunate nature this bidding for Thomson's pulp mill could take on is found in George Smathers' spiral-bound memoirs. Silas A. Jones of Waynesville had requested that Mr. Smathers arrange a meeting with Peter Thomson, so they could talk about a prospective spot for Thomson's pulp mill on Haywood County's Richland Creek. Colonel Jones, as he was called, had come to Waynesville in 1894 from Tampa, Florida, "broken down from over-work from the upbuilding of that state, with nervous prostration complicated with kidney and bladder trouble." Having served

briefly as a young Confederate soldier in the Civil War, he had apparently spent most of his professional career in "upbuilding the Gulf harbors and getting the railroads into Florida." Western North Carolina's mountain climate, pure water, and fresh air had done wonders to restore his health, and he had decided to make it his home.[13] Now, it seemed, he was bent on "upbuilding" this beautiful new country of his by bringing a pulp mill to the banks of Richland Creek.

It was certainly a pretty stream—Richland Creek—but nowhere close to the size needed to supply the large quantity of water necessary to support the pulp-manufacturing processes. Jones was aware of Thomson's sentiments in regard to the water flow, and was primed to discuss the matter when he, Thomson, and Smathers at last got together in Canton. No time was wasted as Jones launched into a proposal that would solve the water problem. By his reckoning, a tunnel could be cut through the Balsam Mountains dividing Richland Creek and the West Fork of the Pigeon River drainages. Water from the West Fork River could then be diverted through the tunnel to sufficiently augment the flow in Richland Creek to support Thomson's mill. It would be as simple as that.

Peter Thomson was unimpressed, however, and pointed out to Colonel Jones that the cost of such an endeavor would be prohibitive. Furthermore, he argued, even if the tunnel was cut through the massive mountain range, from what he knew about the two water bodies and their respective elevations, the combined flow would still not be adequate to support his mill. Attorney Smathers chimed in at about that point with a legal observation that made Jones's idea even less feasible. The land owners along the Pigeon River would undoubtedly object to such a diversion and could rightfully and legally put a stop to it. After that, Jones relented, expressing his hope that if Waynesville could not host Thomson's pulp mill, then he hoped Canton was selected.[14]

George Smathers, who lived in Waynesville and was highly pleased that Thomson was considering locating the plant in Haywood County, felt inclined at one point to promote another place situated more in the center of western North Carolina's spruce belt. Near Ela in Swain County, he told his boss, there was bottom and plateau land available that would make an admirable site for the pulp mill. Abundant supplies of water were available from either the Oconaluftee or Tuckasegee rivers. Furthermore, the site was close to the spruce timber located in the watershed of the Oconaluftee River and the headwaters of Deep Creek, Noland's Creek, Forney Creek, Hazel Creek, and Eagle Creek. Even after hearing other benefits of the Ela location and how some few complications with the railroad could potentially be overcome, Thomson was not convinced.

As Smathers remembered later, Thomson agreed that there were significant advantages to the Ela site. However, just as with the other towns bidding for the mill, railroad access and straightforward routing to Cincinnati along with the appealing prospect of fluming pulpwood out of the Pigeon River headlands

always weighed heavily in Canton's favor. But there was still much to be settled before Canton could be chosen for a pulp mill site. Suitable property for the mill had to be purchased and a contract with the Southern Railway secured.

Obtaining a favorable deal with the railroad company for shipping the pulp to Ohio, as well as delivering supplies, was one of the three requirements Thomson had outlined for Smathers early on. The two men had apparently made some headway with Southern by October, 1905, as can be construed from the following newspaper excerpt: "Mr. Thomson stated that the people of Haywood County are heartily in favor of the enterprise (the pulp mill), and that the Southern Railway has offered many inducements, and that he has their assurance of cooperation in making the mill a success."[15]

Interestingly, just a couple of weeks earlier, another news journal had printed that "a gentleman who is familiar with the operations of the pulp mill people say that the railroad running from Tennessee across the line and two miles into Haywood County, will be extended to Canton."[16] It is not known whether this new railroad option—which involved constructing a line to Waynesville up the torturous gorge carved out by the Pigeon River, and one that would have been in direct competition with the Southern Railway—was ever seriously considered by Thomson and his associates. Nevertheless, the mere fact that this rumor was out there for public consumption and for Southern to contemplate is important. It could possibly have helped Thomson gain the favorable contract that was eventually signed with the Southern Railway.

In March of 1906, several publications reported that the Southern Railway Company had guaranteed to provide fifty cars per day to Thomson's mill to transport the finished product and fifty car loads of incoming freight every day. It was also announced that Southern would soon begin work to improve the railroad between Asheville and Canton on account of the new pulp mill. The summit of the grade just east of Canton would also be cut down fifteen feet, and the Southern's cost for all the railroad work would total $75,000.[17, 18]

By the waning months of 1905, Peter Thomson had succeeded in acquiring the timberlands at the Pigeon headwaters and the railroad company's guarantees—both deemed necessary for selecting Canton as the site to construct his pulp factory. Now, the final requirement for going ahead with his project at Canton was to obtain the land—at a reasonable price—on which his factory buildings and employee houses could be erected. Thomson and George Smathers had not remained idle on this front. With the aid of the Big Five, their negotiations to purchase land on the east side of the Pigeon River had borne fruit by the end of 1905.

Title was secured to a 53-acre tract of land, bounded by the river on the west and railroad to the south. It consisted of parcels purchased from the Big Five men, Dick Hampton and Nelse Mease, and other tracts owned by the Cook heirs, Rices, Moores, and another Canton merchant, Charles T. Wells.[19]

Although these acquisitions allowed sufficient space to construct his mill, Thomson desired more land on the west side of the river where he could store additional pulpwood and build houses for the factory workers. However, complications over price, among other things, held these negotiations in abeyance for some time.

By the end of 1905, surveyors were already hard at work plotting lines across the new mill site. The services of New Yorker George Fiske Hardy had been engaged, and the preeminent engineer and architect of pulp mills in the country had made a preliminary visit to Canton. He wanted to see for himself the low-lying bottom-land that was to support Thomson's immense concrete, brick, and steel structures—and he did not like what he saw! Architect Hardy's arguments against building on the soggy Canton site, primarily because of the significant structural problems that would surely be encountered along the river, failed to impress Peter Thomson. Instead, the wealthy Ohioan ordered the engineering and planning work to proceed as quickly as possible with Canton being the location for his mill.[20] The pulp contract for the coated paper mill in Hamilton would expire on a certain future date, and Thomson was anxious that the Canton pulp mill be up and running by that time in order to supply his Ohio paper machines.[21]

An early completion of Hardy's preliminary engineering drawings was essential to meet the tight schedule and to set crucial steps in motion. These included producing cost estimates, selecting a general contractor, ordering construction materials, and selecting process machinery. Even while the important design

Construction of the cribbed bulkhead along the Champion Fibre Company's property boundary at the Pigeon River began in the winter of 1905–1906. This view from the Southern Railway's iron-truss bridge shows workmen building the double timber walls and filling the space between them with rocks. Men with teams can be seen hauling rocks and dirt on sleds alongside of the structure. Note the farm house in the background which was formerly owned by Dr. Ed Moore, prior to being sold to Thomson. The house survived until about 1910. (from Sellars Collection)

work was progressing in New York, teams of mules and men were at work on the 53-acre construction site, clearing and grading. Photos taken during the winter of 1905–1906 show that one of the first tasks undertaken was constructing a cribbed timber bulkhead along the western waterfront boundary of the property, or river's edge.

Certainly, engineering drawings were not required to take this pragmatic measure to elevate the land, reclaim inundated acreage, and hold back the waters of the Pigeon River. However, the actual building construction could not begin until George Hardy's layouts and foundation plans were ready and a general contractor was hired.

Southern Railroad Map of Western North Carolina — 1900

This map shows Canton and Thomson's Pulp Mill on the Murphy Branch of the Southern RR in relation to other nearby places in western North Carolina. (Original by North Carolina Corporation Commission, prepared by H.C. Brown)

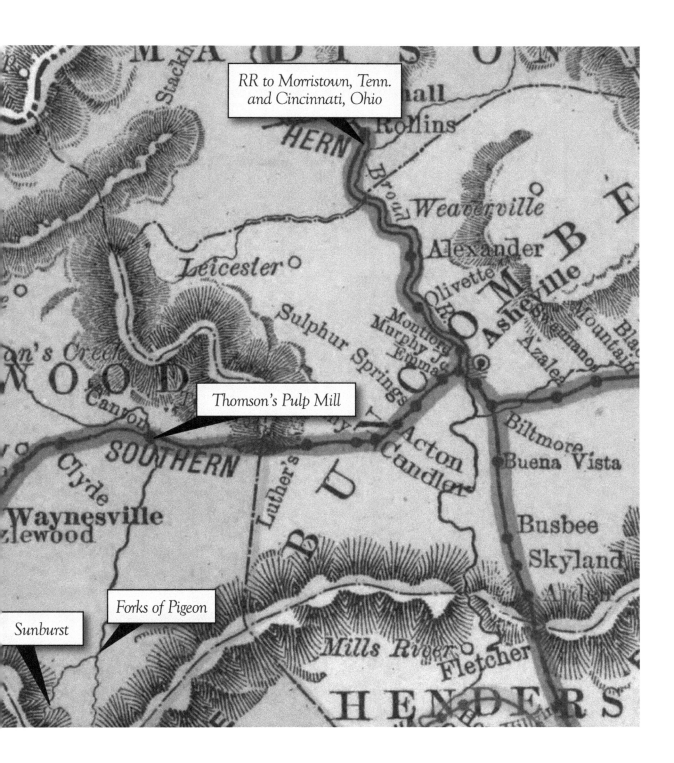

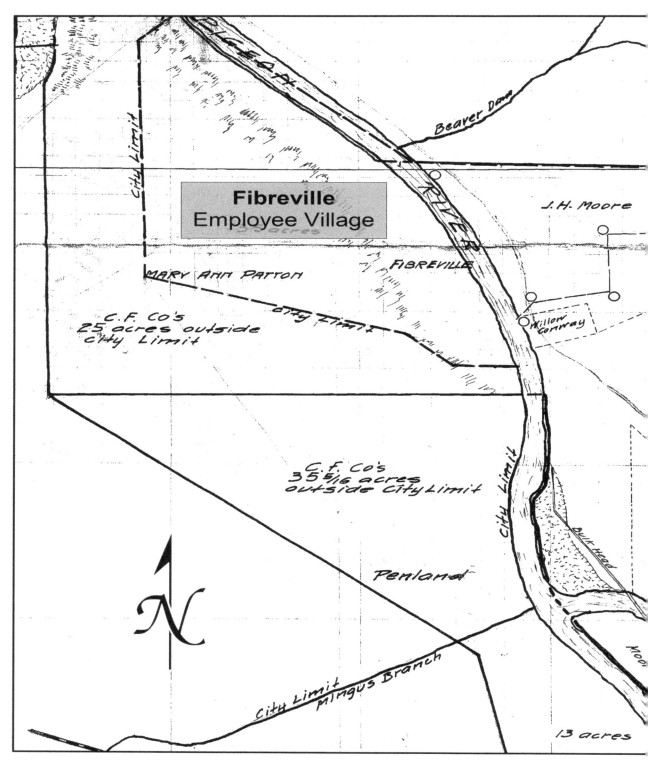

Fibreville
Employee Village

J. H. Moore

Beaver Dam

FIBREVILLE

Willow
Conway

MARY ANN PATTON

City Limit

C.F. Co's
25 acres outside
City Limit

C.F. Co's
35 5/16 acres
outside City Limit

Penland

Bulk Head

Mingus Branch

City Limit

13 acres

(Original from Canton Area Historical Museum)

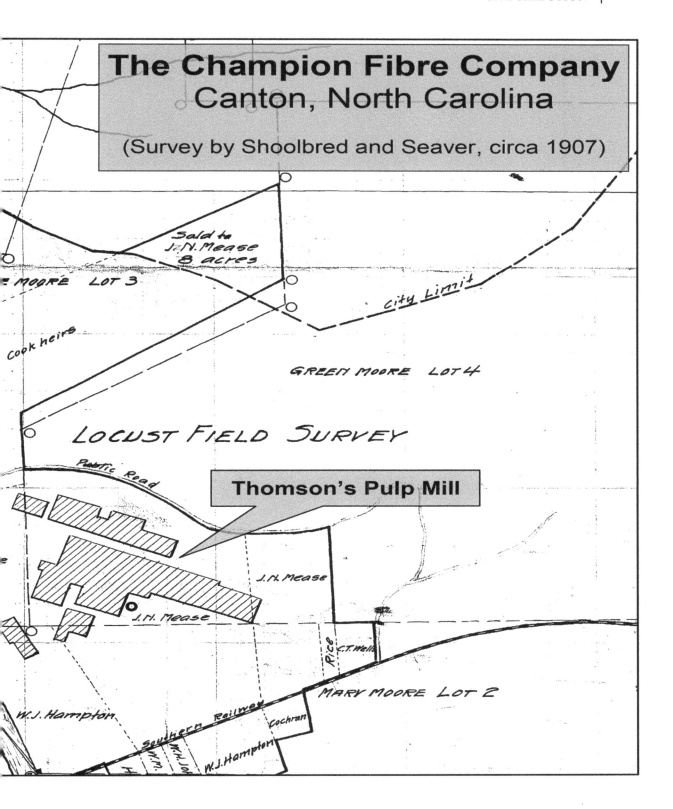

The Champion Fibre Company
Canton, North Carolina

(Survey by Shoolbred and Seaver, circa 1907)

Sold to
J.N. Mease
8 acres

MOORE LOT 3

City Limit

Cook heirs

GREEN MOORE LOT 4

LOCUST FIELD SURVEY

Public Road

Thomson's Pulp Mill

J.N. Mease

J.N. Mease

Rice

C.T. Wells

MARY MOORE LOT 2

W.J. Hampton

Southern Railway

Cochran

W.J. Hampton

In the winter of 1905–1906, the Champion Fibre Company began work on a bulkhead wall along its property boundary at the Pigeon River. Workmen can be seen here constructing the double-wall structure and filling the space between the walls with rocks. (from Canton Area Historical Museum)

Chapter 2
Mobilizing

A January, 1906 newspaper report out of Asheville offered early insight into the construction of Peter Thomson's pulp mill. "The fifty-three acres purchased by the company in Canton and intended for the plant's location is river bottom land and borings have been sufficient to show that the foundations for the contemplated buildings must be largely artificial. If the plant is placed there it will be necessary, it is believed, to drive piling close together in the many acres the buildings will occupy, and great quantities of cement must be used in addition. Such work will be vastly expensive but necessary, because some of the buildings will be 100 feet high and much of the machinery will be of enormous weight."[22]

Although not a professional evaluation, the news account was for the most part accurate. The project's architect/engineer, George Hardy, had himself been to the site, as had his scouts, to investigate and make soil borings to determine the exact geologic conditions of the boggy bottomland along the Pigeon River. To no one's surprise, the engineering investigation proved that piles—many of them—would have to be driven deep into the ground to develop the resistance required to support such enormous mill buildings as Hardy contemplated. But the pile driving could not start until the actual drawings were delivered to the site and a general contractor was hired to execute the extraordinarily difficult and massive work. Thus, besides the ongoing bulkhead construction along the Pigeon River waterfront and general site preparation work, the principal project activities in early 1906 were taking place in Hardy's New York offices.

Preliminary discussions had always considered spruce wood as a must for the **sulphite-pulping process**, which Thomson definitely planned to establish at Canton. He also intended to install a **soda-pulping process**, which was being successfully operated by the New England mills. These northern mills used mostly poplar wood to make the soda pulp and that is what Thomson originally had in mind, with the keen realization that poplar trees abounded across his Pigeon headlands and throughout western North Carolina. However, during architect Hardy's initial design stage, while his draftsmen were beginning to cipher and plot plans for the sulphite and soda pulp mills, Thomson was presented with another unique option by a man named Omega Carr, or "Oma" Carr as he was more commonly called.

Chemical engineer Carr was the Superintendent of the Buena Vista Extract Works in Virginia, and he had been experimenting with the use of chestnut wood chips for making soda pulp, after all the tannin acids had been extracted from them. The extracted acid—or tannin extract—was much valued for its use in the leather tanning industry. At that time, chestnut was the predominant wood of the southern Appalachian region, where numerous factories already produced and concentrated the tannin acids contained in the chestnut wood. The process for doing this was actually of French origin, and consisted of chipping and re-grinding the chestnut wood into very fine fibers—almost

sawdust—and then leaching out the acids in open tubs through a process involving immersion in heated liquors and evaporation. The extracted tannin acid was either dried for transport or loaded in tank cars to be hauled to the tanneries. This common extraction method rendered the spent chestnut fibers useless for making pulp, and the residue was normally burned for fuel at the extract plants.

Oma Carr pitched to Peter Thomson his patented methodology for the double use of the chestnut fiber. His novel idea involved extracting the tannin acids from uniquely prepared chestnut chips and then converting the remaining chestnut fiber into paper pulp. In order to effect this, Carr had also invented and patented a wood-chipping machine that could process chestnut chips into long, thin shavings cut along the wood's grain, rather than across the grain. The inventor/chemist promoted the notion that sales of the tannin extract would pay for the initial supply of chestnut cord wood. It was as if the chestnut wood supply for the soda pulp-making process could be gotten at no cost![23]

Just as Peter Thomson was enchanted with Montgomery Smith's flume scheme, so was he taken with Carr's promising double-use technology. He contracted the services of Oma Carr to oversee the design of a new double-use extract plant at Canton, as well as take on the general management and sales responsibilities for the facility once it was operational. A news article at the time announced that Carr "has accepted the superintendency of a large pulp and extract plant near Asheville, N.C. Mr. Carr is a very ingenious man, and his new plant will be equipped throughout with machinery of his own invention."[24]

In New York, the engineering design work on the extract plant would lag behind the rest of the mill. Hardy and his engineers worked closely with Carr, as they wrestled with converting the inventor's experimental equipment and processes into a fully functioning production operation to be housed in Thomson's brick buildings.

Peter G. Thomson's pulp mill was chartered as an Ohio corporation on January 6, 1906, under the name Champion Fibre Company. Thomson was elected president and Charles S. Bryant was selected for the new secretary and treasurer office. Bryant, a native Ohioan, relocated to Canton a couple of weeks later to join Jim Harris and Oma Carr, who were already on site and busy making plans for the new operation. They set up their headquarters on the construction site in the former residence of Nelse and Nannie Mease, a long structure described as "beporched" in one account (shown on next page). After some minimal remodeling, the house served as the Champion Fibre Company's general offices for the next twelve years.[25] At that time, the foremost decision on the agenda of these Canton Champion men, President Peter Thomson, and architect/engineer George Hardy was the selection of a contractor to build the Champion Fibre

Company pulp factory.

The search for a general contractor did not await completion of George Hardy's design work and final blueprints.[26] In early March, 1906, Mr. Hardy penned a letter to Frank B. Gilbreth, who, like Hardy, was also from New York City. It read in part: "I have today been pleased to receive advice from the Champion Fibre Company that they had executed the contract with you for their new plant at Canton, N.C. I am depending on your giving us good service in this work as you did in constructing the plant for the St. Croix Paper Company..."[27] Although plans for the pulp mill and extract plant were not complete, nor was all of the process equipment purchased, Peter Thomson had gone ahead and selected a contractor. It is ample evidence that he was anxious to get the construction work started. After all, there was a schedule deadline to meet in supplying pulp to his Hamilton coated paper mill.

The contractor he had chosen was Frank Bunker Gilbreth, a former brick mason who was a great believer in scientific management, as it applied to the execution of construction work. Gilbreth had invented novel brick-laying machines and adjustable vertical scaffolding built of pipe frames to facilitate the masons' work. Later in his career, he and his wife Lillian Moller became successful pioneers of time and motion study while, at the same time, raising a family of twelve children. Interestingly, the Gilbreths would become famous in the book and the Hollywood

After some remodeling work, this "beporched" former home of Nelse and Nannie Mease served as the general offices for the Champion Fibre Company during the early years. (from Canton Area Historical Museum)

movie named *Cheaper by the Dozen.*

Frank Gilbreth's preference for working with engineers, architects, and owners on a "cost-plus-fixed sum" basis was promoted in the country's leading journals. He declared this method to be the most satisfactory and economical way to contract building work. There would be no fear of charges for extra work by the parties involved and, importantly, the plans need not be rushed to completion before the excavation was begun.[28] However, an observer to the contract negotiations later noted that this was not exactly the type of contract executed between Thomson and Gilbreth.

The setting for a contract negotiation could not have been finer, although it was held in the dead of winter in January or February of 1906. Peter Thomson hosted George Hardy and Frank Gilbreth at Laurel Court, his new opulent house located just north of Cincinnati at College Hill. At the time, this residence (shown on page 23) was regarded as the most magnificent private residence in the United States west of New York.[29] It was in this palatial venue that the three men, along with Thomson's young son-in-law, Reuben B. Robertson, and most likely lawyers representing each party, convened to discuss the construction of the Canton pulp mill.

Robertson, whose marriage to Hope Thomson was less than a year old, later observed that the discussions between owner, architect/engineer, and contractor resulted in a contract that could best be described as a cost-plus-percentage arrangement. It was not the cost-plus-fixed sum that Gilbreth had touted in the newspapers and trade journals—one in which the contractor's profit would be a pre-established fixed sum. Instead, Gilbreth was to receive a percentage of the entire cost of construction, without a limit on his compensation. It was an agreement that would prove very costly to Champion, Robertson later lamented.[30]

The actual contract between Champion Fibre and Gilbreth Construction has not been discovered, but evidence revealed in an old, injured workman's law suit has shed much light on the contractual details. Peter Thomson did not relinquish complete control of the construction project to Gilbreth. In fact, the contract allowed the owner and engineer to maintain significant authority over the work organization and execution. The key contract stipulations with which Thomson and Hardy retained control included the following:

- *The architect will be represented at the work by a civil engineer, and no alterations shall be made in the work except upon written order of the architect or engineer.*
- *The contractor shall provide sufficient, safe, and proper facilities at all times...and shall follow his [either the architect or engineer] directions regarding the manner in which the work shall be carried out.*
- *The contractor is to carry liability and fire insurance to the extent approved by the owner, and the actual cost of the same is to be borne by the owner.*

- *None of the work included in this contract is to be sublet without the approval of the owner.*
- *It is understood that the contractor shall do all scheduling of materials and obtain all proposals. These proposals to be submitted to the owner and the final purchasing to be done by the contractor or by the owner at the option of the owner, but in any case the owner is to pay the contractor his percentage of profit, which is to be reckoned on their actual cost.*[31]

Although Gilbreth's control over the construction work was limited with this particular contractual arrangement, the measures were not unusual for the day. Furthermore, he was very careful to preserve his right to a percentage of the actual cost of the work.

Upon his first visit to Canton in March of 1906, Frank Gilbreth and some men from his firm made a study of the site and local conditions, including the accessibility of railroad facilities, local supplies of horse and mule teams, and means of conveying freight material. Additionally, they also made a thorough examination of the labor situation as related to laborers, housing, and organized labor conditions. While at Canton and in route to and from New York, these men began hastily studying methods of construction and developing an organization to execute the work.[32]

At the same time, work on the waterfront bulkhead continued and teams of men and horses were being recruited to

Laurel Court, the palatial estate of Peter and Laura Thomson in College Hill, Ohio, hosted the construction contract negotiations with Frank B. Gilbreth in early 1906. (from Canton Area Historical Museum)

clear and level the construction ground so the surveyors could lay out the work. John N. Shoolbred of Waynesville, Captain William H. Hargrove from "up the river" near Forks of Pigeon, Tommie Remson, and possibly other "field engineers" faced very important responsibilities for the construction work.[33] They had to read and interpret Hardy's early plans, then stake the building lines and establish reference monuments and other controls to guide the constructors.

These initial activities to advance Thomson's great Canton enterprise did not escape the notice of alert local men and women. Their suspicions were further aroused when the following headline appeared in a March 11, 1906 Asheville newspaper: "Champion Fibre Company Prepares to Begin Work."[34] Additionally, journals far and wide began to advertise Gilbreth

A dark but revealing photo looking northwest shows the early construction site in about April, 1906. Construction sheds, timber piles lying on the ground, and at least four steam-driven pile drivers can be seen. As of yet, no brick structures have risen out of the muddy river bottomland. (from Sellars Collection)

Construction's urgent need for workers. Ads such as the one below were common:

WANTED–Competent men wanted at Canton and at Champion for construction work on the pulp mill plant...Also good log and timber cutters, cattle drivers, steam shredder operators. Good foremen in all departments. Come in person. No use to write letters.[35]

Yet, workmen were not the only flesh and blood commodities in demand. Horse, mule, and oxen teams were very much needed to do the heavy hauling, grading, and sometimes lifting chores that were ever increasing as the construction activity began to ramp up. Thus,

solicitations for teams, like the one below, routinely appeared in the local papers.

WANTED–Teams, steady work for the summer for good teams. Wages from $2.50 to $3.00 per day. The Champion Fibre Co., Canton, N.C.[36]

When the first drawing with the main pulp mill foundation details arrived at the job site, James F. Powers—who was Gilbreth Construction's general superintendent in charge of the construction work—and his foremen must have studied it with some degree of awe and disbelief. Thousands of wood piles were shown that would have to be driven into the soft ground. Once these were sunk, it would be necessary to clear away the water and mud from the tops of the piles so that substantial concrete foundations could be poured over them. It was imperative that this work be executed properly and exactly as the drawings indicated. The construction bosses realized that the piling and foundations would have to bear immense loads of heavy process machinery and massive brick walls rising to heights of more than a hundred feet.

Numbers and lettering scrawled across Hardy's initial foundation drawing indicated the location and spacing of the piling. Also, the draftsman was very careful to specify the design loads of each pile, which varied in weight from three, nine, ten, sixteen, seventeen, and eighteen tons. Superintendent Power's team was tasked with tedious and time-consuming exercises of performing load tests to determine the exact depths that the wood piles would need to be driven in order to support the anticipated extreme weights. Once the proof tests were completed, the supervisors quickly determined that more than forty miles of piling would have to be pounded into the ground by the job's end. Certainly it must have seemed a daunting task, but the construction bosses ordered the work to proceed on the deep foundations.

Gilbreth Construction had five steam-driven pile drivers shipped to Canton by rail, and these were soon puffing and pounding away at different locations across the construction site. At first, mostly local men were recruited to operate the machinery and do the man-handling work. They built skid works, chopped pointed ends on the timber piles, rigged piles and steadied them in place, spliced piles when necessary to reach greater depths, stoked and operated the steam engines, and dragged the pile drivers over skid logs into position time and time again for every pile that was driven. A great many of these hands were farmers, whose only experience with "public work," as they called it, and working under the supervision of a boss was the county road maintenance work. One or two days per year the men were required to labor on road crews to pay off their annual road tax.

The work on Thomson's pulp mill provided the local farmers and farm hands with much-needed extra income. But their experience with regular hours of employment was scant, and they still had to attend to their farms. It soon became apparent to Gilbreth's supervisory team that the men could not always be counted on. Farm chores seemed to take precedent over the construction work, especially during that first spring planting season. Foremen complained that in order to keep the job going and maintain the schedule, they needed three crews: one coming, one going, and one at work. After the first month or two, it became plainly obvious that a more reliable work force would have to be found. Eventually, laborers and skilled craftsmen from Boston, New York, Chicago, and other places throughout the eastern part of the country, along with many foreigners, were hired to get the building work out of the muddy ground and on schedule.[37, 38]

Up at Sunburst, Montgomery Smith kept the steam-driven sawmill busy slicing logs into boards needed at the Canton mill for many purposes: constructing the new waterfront bulkhead, concrete forms, scaffolding, and the shacks and storage sheds that were being hurriedly thrown up by Gilbreth. Additionally, Smith's loggers were hustling to find the stoutest and straightest trees in the woods, these to be cut and hauled to Canton for use as piling. Transporting both lumber and tree piles down the river to Canton was another matter, however. The road from the Three Forks region was not only narrow and winding, but it included several fords. During rainy periods, it was not uncommon for Sunburst mule teams to become mired up to their bellies, while the heavily-loaded wagons sank to the axles. Not only that, the fording spots often became too treacherous to safely negotiate. This bad road was a real challenge in the early days of the mill construction, but everyone recognized that the Smith log flume would eventually solve that problem.

Meanwhile, Gilbreth Construction determined that a more dependable source of lumber had to be found in order that the production could be closely controlled and delays eliminated. An up-to-date, steam-powered sawmill operation was erected on site, right in the middle of the construction work.[39] In many of the surviving construction photos of this period, the sawmill's tall stacks are visible and usually spewing black smoke. Foremen's orders for boards to build concrete forms, shoring, scaffolding, access ramps, framing, flooring, and roofing, among other

things, could be quickly filled on demand by the mill. There would be no end to the frenzied lumber cutting until the last batches of concrete had been poured and roofing installed on the highest buildings and conveyor houses.

While the piling work was progressing, the Southern Railway supported the construction activity with sidetracks to allow shipment of materials to locations near the work or to the storage yards. In the spring of 1906, the Southern announced that the project to improve the railroad from Asheville to Canton would soon get underway. Included in this $75,000 project was an initiative to reduce the steep grade into Canton, so that longer trains of cars could be pulled into and out of the town. This involved lowering the cut just east of the Southern depot by about fifteen feet. A contract was awarded to Henderson, Ramsey and Company of Asheville for the removal of 237,000 cubic yards of rock and dirt. As might be expected, a steam shovel was brought in by train to excavate the material, causing many months of congested affairs around Canton's railroad depot. Interestingly, the excavated material was hauled only a short distance away and used to backfill behind the new waterfront bulkhead along the Pigeon River.[40, 41, 42]

Construction of Champion Fibre Company's mill was well underway by mid-1906. Outside blood was being mobilized every day to augment the local labor forces who were working at a hectic pace to sink the piles into the ground. Additionally,

This appears to be a piling load test, surely ordered by one of George F. Hardy's engineers. Timbers have been stretched across selected piles previously driven into the ground. On top of these wood beams, masons are laying up a solid mass of heavy brick work to determine how much weight the piles would support. This was the only way the engineers could confidently predict that the piles were being driven deep enough to bear the enormous loads of the buildings and equipment. (from Sellars Collection)

skilled craftsmen including masons, carpenters, ironworkers, and mechanics were being sought and found in places as far west as Chicago and the far corners of the world. The fruits of these men's labor were beginning to show, as wooden scaffolding and brick walls were now poking out of the boggy ground. Exceptional rainfall events were not helping things, though. After extended periods of wet weather, the low-lying construction site became a sea of mud, one source recalled. Of course the conditions of the road from Sunburst to Canton became even worse, but that situation was about to be remedied. Just as soon as Peter Thomson and attorney George Smathers obtained the last right-of-way, the much-anticipated log flume could be built.[43]

Delivery of lumber and pulp wood from the remote sawmill village of Sunburst (shown here) to Canton proved to be extremely problematic for the Champion Fibre Company. (from Canton Area Historical Museum)

Chapter 3
Smith's Flume and
the Pigeon River Railway

Ever since Montgomery Smith mentioned the tantalizing possibility of fluming pulpwood to the Canton mill site, Peter Thomson was obsessed with the idea. In fact, he had counted on that specific scheme when judging Canton favorably against other places vying for his pulp mill. When satisfied that his three main requirements to locate at Canton had been met, or soon would be—those being possession of the timberlands at the Pigeon headlands, the Canton property, and favorable railroad rates—Thomson directed his attention to obtaining necessary rights-of-way to build the flume. The wooden plank structure would stretch for a distance of about sixteen miles. Its path was intended to run for ten miles from Sunburst down the West Fork of the Pigeon River to Forks of Pigeon.[44] Then from the Forks it would follow a course beside the Pigeon River for another six miles to Canton.

George Smathers distinctly remembered how Montgomery Smith assured Peter Thomson that a thorough investigation of constructing the flume had been made and the plan would undoubtedly be a success. Smith had employed an elderly man by the name of "Dobbs," or "Hobbs," to survey the line, as Smathers later recollected, and the surveyor reported a fall in the elevation of the river about twice what was later ascertained.[45] Smathers' further investigative diligence on the matter soon led him to suspect something was awry.

Discussions with a few prominent citizens of Haywood County, all of whom lived on the Pigeon River—men such as Captain William Ledbetter, Captain William Harrison Hargrove, and Mr. D.N. Kinsland—revealed a contrary view of the flume scheme. These wise men expressed an opinion that from Sunburst down to Forks of Pigeon—where the east and west forks converge to form the Pigeon River—there was probably enough fall in the waters for the flume to work. However, from Forks of Pigeon to Canton, a distance of about six miles, it was their assessment that the Pigeon River was too flat for the successful operation of a flume.

Waynesville engineer John N. Shoolbred was hired to hurriedly survey the entire route of the flume along the river from Canton to Sunburst. Surveyors William H. Hargrove and Tommie Remson were assigned the project and by February, 1906, they had established the flume line that permitted legal rights-of way to be finalized. Evidently, this survey was made in great haste and did not

This is the type of wooden-plank log flume envisioned by Montgomery Smith and Peter G. Thomson to transport pulpwood from Sunburst to the Champion Fibre Company in Canton. The beneficial prospects for such a flume helped convince Thomson to build his pulp mill at Canton. (from Canton Area Historical Museum)

include a measurement of the gradient along its route.

Mr. Smith stood by his conviction in the flume project, even after attorney Smathers relayed the doubtful opinions of the local men to his and Smathers' boss. Although surely fearful that there might be some truth to this latest intelligence, Peter Thomson and George Smathers began canvassing land-owners along the Hargrove-Remson flume route to secure rights-of-way for the flume. In a few cases they were received inhospitably, meeting skepticism and down-right opposition from the farmers—so much so that Montgomery Smith was moved to write a scathing letter to Colonel Silas Jones in Waynesville.

It is quite likely that Smith intended for his grim sentiments to be published, because the entire letter found its way into the local Asheville paper by mid-February, 1906. Smith wrote in part:

"I know you [Jones] *will feel chagrinned at the now almost certain loss of that enterprise* [pulp mill] *to your county by reason of the organized hold-up instituted by a few selfish people who think they see a chance to get something for nothing."*

After explaining that the company could simply bottle up the timber on the Pigeon headlands for years to come and draw on other resources, he added,

"The local problems of Canton have been enough to cause the most serious consideration of a change of location, and if the flume trans-portation must be abandoned and a railroad built then there would be no particular gain in stopping at Canton and the cars just as well go on down Pigeon River via the Tennessee and North Carolina Railroad [a proposed railroad line at that time] *to Newport, Tenn., or to Asheville as the advantage of either site may determine...The final efforts in the coming weeks will determine the flume question.*[46]

It is not known what effect Smith's letter of warning had on the stubborn farmers who were holding out for more money or better deals. Nevertheless, by the end of February, Thomson and Smathers had obtained the signatures of all but three of the landowners along the flume route. The holdouts were John Plott, Wiley Henson, and Mrs. Holtzclaw, a widow with whom extended negotiations ensued for several months. Plott owned and operated a mill on the West Fork and he was eventually satisfied with a payment of $650. The money was meant to be a compensation for the damages he would sustain resulting from water being diverted from his mill to the flume. According to Attorney George Smathers, Henson required more personal attentions from the Big Five and the "Big Man" Thomson himself. After a house visit from Thomson, during which Henson revealed that the source of his failing health and woes was the rheumatism contracted while lying in the Petersburg trenches during the Civil War, a meeting of the minds was reached.[47] In exchange for Henson's granting a right-of-way, Thomson paid him $200 for damages and agreed to supply shingles from his shingle machine at Sunburst to cover Henson's unfinished barn.

An agreement with the widow Holtzclaw in Canton was finally reached in late June, 1906, thus securing rights-of-way for the entire length of the flume. The satisfaction that Thomson must have felt was short-lived however. By then, additional surveys of the gradient along the flume line revealed what others had suspected, but Thomson and Smith had refused to believe. It was determined that in order to build the flume on the proper grade, such that pulpwood could be sluiced down to Canton, the flume would have to be one hundred and fifty feet high at Forks of Pigeon. The required elevated flume structures from Sunburst all the way to Canton would be prohibitively expensive to build. Moreover, the several rights-of-way for the flume were not wide enough to allow such a substantial structure to be constructed.[48]

The disappointment, and probably anger, that filled Peter Thomson upon receiving this report can only be imagined. His faith in Montgomery Smith's log flume idea had been ill-placed. It was late summer, 1906 and too late to back away from the Canton decision. Great efforts and expenditures were already being made at that place toward constructing his mill. As difficult as it must have been, Thomson had to abandon all further consideration of fluming wood from the Pigeon headwaters. This meant, of course, that an alternative method of reliably accessing his 40,000 acres of reserve timberlands would have to be found, and soon. Besides

that, it was now more important than ever to obtain adequate supplies of pulpwood on the open market to support the pulp mill and extract operations at Canton.

The head men of the company at that time—Peter Thomson, Jim Harris, Oma Carr, Secretary/Treasurer Charles Bryant, and Montgomery Smith—reckoned the value of the timber reserves held in the Pigeon headlands was too substantial to leave stranded and uncut. Funds from the sale of this timber could be used to pay for the completion of the Champion Fibre Company's new mill, among other things. But it would have to be gotten out somehow other than the doomed flume scheme or the unreliable river road. So it was ultimately decided by Thomson and his associates that the most practical method of reaching and marketing these valuable timber holdings was to build a standard gauge railroad up the river, from Canton all the way to Sunburst.

George Smathers was directed to handle the legal affairs for establishing a railroad, and in November, 1906 he successfully obtained a state charter for the Pigeon River Railway Company. Incorporation papers were immediately filed in the Haywood County courthouse, establishing the railroad as a common carrier—one that carried not only freight but passengers as well. Capital stock in the company was valued at $200,000, and the first company officers elected were President Oma Carr, Vice-President Reuben B. Robertson, and Secretary/Treasurer Charles S. Bryant. Classification

Reuben B. Robertson was first sent to western North Carolina in 1906 by his father-in-law to help secure rights-of-way for the Pigeon River Railway's Sunburst-to-Canton railroad. The twenty-seven year old Cincinnati lawyer could not have known that this early work would lead to a providential professional career, affecting thousands upon thousands of western North Carolinians. (from Canton Area Historical Museum)

of the railroad as a common carrier made it possible to build and operate the railroad through private properties against the landowners' wishes. Although this right of "eminent domain" granted the company significant power and legal authority to impose their will on the Pigeon Valley farmers, it was resorted to in only one instance.[49, 50]

John N. Shoolbred from Waynesville was hired to survey and locate the railroad line from Canton to Sunburst. Not far behind the

surveyors, attorney Smathers began tirelessly pursuing rights-of-way for the railroad bed. However, he was not working alone. Ably assisting him was Reuben B. Robertson, who had been assigned the responsibility by his father-in-law. During that same time period, Peter Thomson may have been suffering from ill health. It was said that Thomson had sailed to Turkey sometime in August to buy furnishings for his new Ohio mansion, Laurel Court, and to visit friends who were consular representatives in that country. Apparently, he was stricken with malarial fever during the voyage and his health likely deteriorated from that affliction.[51] At any rate, Thomson did not personally involve himself in the railroad right-of-way acquisitions, as he had done for the flume. Instead, he sent his young son-in-law into the mountains to work with George Smathers. So began Reuben Robertson's crucial involvement with the building and subsequent operation of the Champion mill.

Robertson recounted later that he and Smathers spent week after long week traveling up and down the Pigeon River Valley, negotiating with the farmers for the rights-of-way and haggling over the damages to be paid to the property owners. He especially remembered the three "Captains" who lived in the Forks of Pigeon area, otherwise known as Bethel. These former Confederate soldiers—Captain Thomas B. Edmonston, Captain William Bradley Ledbetter, and Captain William Stewart Terrell—were now elderly men who were held in high esteem by their neighbors. Settlements were amicably reached with

Edmonston and Terrell. Captain Edmonston considered the railroad to be an asset to the community and offered a right-of-way at no cost. Captain Terrell, on the other hand, was not so liberal minded and demanded a payment equal to the fair market value of the property taken.

Captain Ledbetter, who had more acreage affected by the railroad intrusion, was a much harder nut to crack. He refused to accept Smathers' and Robertson's reasoning that the railroad would save him money by reducing the cost of transporting his products and supplies. The captain was not convinced at all, and countered with his opinion that the railroad would be well-nigh ruinous to him. He currently had profitable markets in the local area for his large corn crops, and the railroad would surely bring in competitive corn at lower costs. In the end, this nut indeed proved too difficult to crack. It was the only case where the railroad company had to use its power of eminent domain, securing property through condemnation proceedings.

Reuben Robertson's recollection of dealing with these three captains failed to take

William Harrison Hargrove was one of the four "captains" that George Smathers and Reuben B. Robertson dealt with in their efforts to secure rights-of-way for the Pigeon River Railroad. Hargrove was about sixty-five years old at that time and employed as a surveyor by the Champion Fibre Company. Although often referred to as "Captain Hack," he only rose to the rank of first lieutenant during his four years of service with the Confederate 25th N.C. Infantry Regiment. After the war he farmed, taught school, served as Haywood County's Surveyor, was elected to represent the county at the State General Assembly, held the state's highest office in the Sons of Temperance organization, and became the railroad's first station agent when it reached Pigeon River (Canton) in 1882. Following the start-up of the Champion Fibre Company, Hargrove briefly managed and edited the Canton Vindicator newspaper until his eventful life finally ran its course in 1909. Hargrove was described as a "useful citizen" by one obituarist, but even that high judgment seems to be understated. (from collection of Carroll C. Jones)

into account the dealings with another troublesome captain living in Bethel at that time. But George Smathers distinctly remembered this fourth captain whose name was William Harrison Hargrove, or Hack as he was commonly known. Although Captain Hargrove was a surveyor employed by the Champion Fibre Company, he still was unwilling to accept the amount of damages offered in compensation for the railroad running through his property. However, Hargrove agreed to arbitration and the arbitrators eventually awarded an amount between what the captain felt the damages were worth and the railroad was offering.[52, 53]

While these old rebel captains were being dealt with and rights-of-way secured, Shoolbred completed the railroad survey, including a profile of the line to be built. Rough cost estimates for the railroad were coming in at $8,000 to $9,000 per mile of track.[54] In March, 1907, a contract was awarded to the firm of W.J. Oliver Company out of Knoxville, Tennessee, for the grading and building of a roadbed from Canton to Sunburst. Oliver was well-known and had a substantial amount of work in progress. Because this firm was on the verge of dedicating their resources to a much larger contractual undertaking—construction of the Panama Canal—the relatively modest project on the Pigeon River Railway was sublet to Yandle Brothers, also out of Knoxville.

At the time, Yandle was involved in double-tracking the Southern lines from Asheville to Morristown, Tennessee. The grading work up the Pigeon River Valley

was a straight-forward proposition and a job that this firm anticipated could be executed with dispatch. Plans were immediately set in motion to send a large force of men and much equipment to Canton to get the job started. Several camps were to be established along the Pigeon and West Fork rivers and up to four hundred mules kept at work. So by early spring of 1907, clearing and dangerous dynamite-blasting activities had gotten underway on the badly needed railroad.[55]

Things were being pushed ahead as rapidly as possible, but whether or not the Pigeon River Railway would be completed by the end of 1907 and in time to supply pulpwood to the operations at Canton was very much up in the air. Certainly, no one anticipated the coming crisis and its resulting dire consequences.

Three Gilbreth pile-driving machines are shown hammering away in this photo. The men in the foreground are using axes to chop pointed ends on the timber piles. (from Sellars Collection)

Chapter 4
Thomson's Pulp Mill

The great works at Canton that early reports labeled "Thomson's Pulp Mill" and that Thomson himself called the "Champion Fibre Company Pulp Factory" were actually two plants—a pulp-making plant and a tannin extract plant. The pulp mill envisioned by Thomson and that George Hardy was commissioned to design included both sulphite and soda pulp-making processes, capable of producing a combined 200 tons per day of high-quality pulp. In the beginning, the intention had been to use primarily spruce wood in the sulphite-pulping process and poplar wood in the soda process. However, the abundant supplies of chestnut wood in western North Carolina had driven the decision to adopt Oma Carr's "double-use" technology. Short-fiber soda pulp would be produced from chestnut chips after the tannin acids were extracted. One news outlet of the day boiled the matter down thusly: "The new methods look to the extraction of the tannic acid and the use of the resultant pulp in paper making. The result will be a savings of the potentialities of the wood which heretofore have been wasted."[56]

Consequently, instead of using poplar wood to produce soda pulp, the new plan was to use the chestnut fiber left over from Carr's tannin extraction process. Carr had convinced Mr. Thomson that the sales of tannin extract would offset the cost of the chestnut wood supply. In other words, the soda pulp mill could be supplied at essentially no cost! This enticing notion of Oma Carr's had been too good to pass up.

Architect Hardy separated the pulp mill and tannin extract plants with his design layout. On the south side of several lines of railroad sidetracks he located a large grouping of brick buildings that comprised the pulp mill. Housed in these structures were the sulphite and soda-pulping processes, pulp bleaching and drying equipment, a pulp storage warehouse, the main boiler house with a towering concrete smokestack, and an electric-generating facility. On the north side of the tracks he laid out a smaller cluster—or lineup—of brick buildings associated with the tannin extract plant. Within these masonry walls were a barking, chipping, and regrinder operations; pulp leaching tanks and equipment; evaporators; and more boilers for burning bark and wood refuse.

George Hardy also made plans for separate facilities on the periphery of these two plants. A pump house was located on the bank of the river to charge the mill water supply and to fill a reservoir on a neighboring hill north of the extract plant. This reservoir had the capacity to store up to 300,000 gallons of water for fire protection purposes. In addition, a large complex for barking, sawing, and chipping pulpwood was strategically positioned on the southwest side of the property where pulpwood in vast quantities could be conveniently stored along railroad sidetracks.

Those were the original components that comprised Thomson's pulp mill and extract plant. Inside the substantial brick structures were housed state-of-the-art machinery and piping associated with the pulping and extraction processes. These processes are further described below.

The **sulphite-pulping process** had been around since 1867 and primarily used spruce wood to make sulphite pulp, as Thomson and Hardy intended for the Champion Fibre pulp mill. Hemlock and balsam were also suitable woods that could be converted to pulp through this process. Although considerably simplified, the following basic steps were involved in the sulphite chemical and mechanical process planned for the Champion Fibre Company:

- The pulpwood is sawn into bolts (short lengths of logs), de-barked, and reduced to chips. These chips are then screened and conveyed to storage bins above the three large digesters—or "cooking" vessels.
- An acidic cooking liquor is made from burning sulphur to produce sulphur dioxide and then mixing this off-gas with water and lime.
- Each large, lead-lined steel digester vessel is filled with wood chips from the overhead bins and with the acidic sulphurous cooking liquor.
- Live steam is introduced into the digester and the pressure is held constant at 75 to 80 pounds per square inch, while the temperature is allowed to rise to about 300 degrees Fahrenheit. Sulphur

dioxide gas is constantly vented to capture tanks and liquor buildup is relieved out of the top of the digester. This cooking—or digesting—process removes the undesirable lignin from the cellulose fibers.

- Upon completion of the cook, usually seven to nine hours, a large valve is opened in the bottom of the digester and its contents are blown through a pipe into a blow-pit and thoroughly washed.

- The used—or black—liquor is pumped to a recovery process, and the cooked cellulose fiber, or pulp, is processed through specialized equipment where it is screened and filtered, bleached, thickened, dried, and packaged for shipment.[57]

The **soda-pulping process,** patented in 1854, varied somewhat from the sulphite process. Most importantly, the species of wood fiber was different, as was the makeup of cooking liquor. Champion Fibre Company's plans were to use chestnut wood in its soda-pulping process. Also, rather than an acidic sulphurous cooking liquor, the soda process used caustic soda to cook with. The steps involved in the soda process planned at Thomson's pulp mill were basically as follows:

- After extracting the tannin acids from chestnut chips, the wet leached chips are dried and then conveyed to storage bins over the seven large steel digester vessels.

- Each digester vessel is filled with chestnut chips from the overhead bins and with caustic soda cooking liquor.

- Live steam is injected into the digester and the caustic cooking liquor is circulated as thoroughly as possible. The internal pressure is held to about 100 pounds per square inch, as gases and air are relieved from the top of the vessel.

- Upon completion of the cook, which might be approximately six hours depending on cooking conditions such as temperature and pressure, the cooked contents are blown into the blowpit and washed with warm water.

- The used (black) liquor is pumped to a recovery process, and the cooked chestnut cellulose fiber, or pulp, is processed through a similar progression of specialized pulp-processing equipment as used in the sulphite pulping process.[58]

Oma Carr's **tannin extract process** was not only novel, but it was a proprietary one which employed his own patents. Primarily, it involved his methods for manufacturing paper-pulp from chestnut wood, after extracting and preserving the tannin acids. This extract could be sold very profitably to the leather industry to be used in tanning leather. Champion

Fibre's extract plant also pioneered Carr's patented wood chipper to produce uniform and uniquely-shaped chip shavings that helped preserve the integrity of the wood fibers. The steps involved in the process that Carr and George Hardy worked out were as follows:

- Chestnut pulpwood is received at the plant in bolts (short lengths of logs), where it is de-barked, cut into billets (small chunks of wood), and fed into the Carr chippers. The chips are cut parallel to the grain, or with the grain, to produce the required thin shavings.

- Chips thus prepared are then sent to large concrete tubs (seventy-two of them in Thomson's pulp mill) fitted with mechanisms for heating and circulating hot water and liquors in first a rough-leaching process and finally in a pulp leaching process.

- After the appropriate time for leaching has transpired, all the liquor is drained from the final leaching tanks, then the chestnut chips are dried and conveyed to the soda digesters.

- The leaching liquor is pumped to four copper evaporators where the water gets evaporated and the extracted tannin residue is collected, packaged, and shipped to customers.[59]

Descriptions of the original mill, surviving drawings, and photographs indicate that there were twenty-five buildings associated with the main pulp mill. Just to the north of this large grouping of buildings—across several railroad sidetracks—stood the tannin extract plant, consisting of seven buildings. Almost all of the many structures situated across thirteen acres of river bottomland were made of brick and topped out with either reinforced concrete, plank-on-timber, or sheet iron roofs. The two digester buildings were exceptional in that the brick walls were two feet thick. When completed, their several stories reached dizzying heights; the sulphite digester house was 122 feet high, and at the time was the tallest industrial building in the state.[60] Only the main boiler house's tall concrete smokestack would reach a loftier height, measuring 250 feet tall and 17 feet in diameter.

George Hardy's specifications for the structural support systems—such as columns, floor beams, and roof structures—had to take into consideration the chemical environment, as well as matters of structural load and stress. His plans usually called for either sawn timber supports or structural steel members, based on the design requirements. Hardy specified either reinforced concrete floors or rough timber flooring, except in the pulp warehouse where finished hardwood flooring was called for on the drawings. He left out no measures in order to construct enormous buildings that could resist the static and dynamic loads of the massive equipment and piping installations, the corrosive chemicals involved in the manufacturing processes, extreme weather conditions, and, of course, fire. To minimize damage inflicted by this last inevitable hazard, Hardy planned automatic sprinkler systems for virtually every building.

Architect/Engineer Hardy ordered twenty coal-fired boilers from the Heine Safety Boiler Company for the main boiler house, and these would provide the necessary "high pressure" steam to power two large electric generation units. The excess steam was sent through pressure-reducing valves and combined with the steam produced by the extract plant's refuse boilers. This "low pressure" steam supply was then piped throughout the mill to satisfy the significant heating demands of the various pulping and tannin extract processes. Of course, electricity produced by the two generators was used for lighting and to power the majority of the mechanical equipment in the pulp mill and extract plant. Exceptions were the variable-speed machines which were driven by steam engines. A contract with the Haywood Electric Power Company of Waynesville provided a back-up supply of electricity of up to 1,500 horsepower. To meet this demand, the utility concern planned to spend $40,000 on an expansion of their facilities.[61, 62] Certainly, Thomson's pulp mill would not want for electricity and horsepower, and virtually all of the space under roof was lit up with artificial illumination.

In addition to the pulping machinery

and steam and power generation facilities, there was a need to move raw materials, products, and refuse from place to place. Hardy designed an extensive system of conveyors to transport wood, chips, bark, refuse (sawdust and shavings), coal, and ash to and from the various stages of the many processes. Elevated conveyors and a bucket elevator transferred the screened spruce, hemlock, and balsam chips from the wood preparation buildings directly to the storage bins over the sulphite digesters. Another elevated and completely housed conveyor stretched 520 feet long and moved spruce, hemlock, and balsam refuse from the wood preparation buildings to the tannin extract plant. There, conveyors distributed the refuse to the plant's boilers to be burned as fuel, or to storage bins and leaching tanks. Similarly, chestnut refuse was either conveyed to the plant's boilers or to the leaching tanks. Conveyors also carried clean chestnut chips from Carr's chippers and the regrinders to the leaching tanks. Finally, conveyors positioned underneath the leaching tanks transferred leached chestnut chips to a series of other conveyors for transport to the soda digesters.[63]

A comprehensive listing of all the buildings that comprised the original Champion Fibre Company pulp mill can be found on the following pages.[64]

Pulp Mill

Building	Details
Wood Preparation (2 buildings)	80x100 and 75x100: Two stories with brick walls and mill construction.
Sulphite Digester House	118x33x122-ft high: Several stories of brick construction with three heavy-steel, lead-lined digesters, each 16-ft diameter and 54-ft high. Chip bins are located overhead and building is topped with monitor roof for ventilation.
Sulphite Blow Tanks	46x118: One story of mill construction containing three blow tanks, each 32-ft diameter and 22-ft high. Building is topped with monitor roof for ventilation.
Lime Slaking and Storage	82x53: Two stories of reinforced concrete and steel construction.
Sulfur Storage	36x53: One story of reinforced concrete and steel construction.
Sulfur Burning	39x53: One story of reinforced concrete and steel construction.
Lime Storage	40x48: One story of reinforced concrete and steel construction.
Chemical Storage	125x75: Two and three stories high with second floor of reinforced concrete supported by pin-connected girder frames.
Causticizing	108x75: Two stories of reinforced concrete floors and a concrete roof with large skylights supported by steel trusses. Contains twenty-six causticizing tanks, each 15.5-feet diameter.
Soda Evaporator Room	45x62: One story of brick construction and wood roof, containing four evaporators, each 9-ft diameter and 17-ft long.
Reclaiming Room	96x120: One story of brick construction with concrete roof with large skylights supported by steel trusses. Contains twelve bleaching cells with liquor tanks connecting to them. Also equipped with five 6-ft by 18-ft boilers and five rotary furnaces with fireboxes, all connected to a large smoke flue.
Soda Digester House	146x54x100-ft high: Several stories of brick construction with seven digesters, each 10-ft diameter and 54-ft high. Liquor tanks and chip bins are located overhead and building is topped with monitor roof for ventilation.
Soda Blow Tank / Washing	58x146: Two stories of brick construction, containing blow tanks and massive ventilators, each 16-ft diameter by 90-ft high.
Bleach-Making	85x37: Three stories constructed of reinforced concrete with wood roof, containing reinforced concrete bleach-settling and bleach-storage tanks. Shipping tracks are alongside.
Bleach Storage	54x129: Two stories.
Pulp Bleaching	155x86: Two stories with reinforced concrete second floor and wood roof, containing twenty-four reinforced concrete tanks, each 17-ft diameter and 24-feet high. Second floor is poured across the top of these tanks.
Screen Room	163x73: Two and three stories of brick construction with wood roof supported by steel trusses, containing screening machines and reinforced concrete rifflers, tanks, baffles, etc.
Filter Room	163x56: Two stories of brick construction with wood roof and large skylights, containing large sedimentation basin which runs half the room's length and full width. Balance of building contains reinforced concrete filter tanks for both hot and cold water.

Beater / Wet Machine Room	78x140: Two stories of brick construction with second floor of reinforced concrete and a wood roof supported by steel trusses. Contains beaters and sulphite wet machines.
Machine Room	164x228: Two stories of brick construction with second floor of reinforced concrete and a wood roof with large skylights supported by steel trusses. Contains soda pulp-drying machines, sulphite pulp-drying machines, and board machines on second floor.
Pulp Storage	111x177: Two stories of brick and mill construction throughout with hardwood flooring, wood roof, and large skylight. Separate tracks on trestles located on two sides provide direct shipping of pulp product to Southern Railway sidings.
Main Boiler House	72x184: Two stories of brick construction with reinforced concrete floors and concrete roof supported by steel trusses. Contains Berquist coal bunker with 10,000-tons capacity. Also contains twenty Heine boilers, 316-hp each, with Murphy auto-stoked furnaces. Coal supply comes in along the side of building from cars on a railroad trestle, where it is dropped into a concrete coal bunker. From there the coal is carried via conveyors to another bunker over the boilers and then distributed to auto-stoked furnaces. Refuse ash drops into concrete pits and from there is conveyed automatically to cars.
Smokestack	250-ft high, 17-ft diameter and constructed of 18-in thick, formed-and-poured reinforced concrete walls.
Generator Room	144x63 and 53x37: Two stories with brick walls, reinforced concrete second floor, and steel-truss roof. Contains two large electric-generation units, main electrical switch gear, and a 35-ton traveling crane.
Repair Shop	54x162: One story with brick walls and mill construction.
Pump House	24x54: One story brick construction with steel truss-supported roof, containing one 1,500-gpm Underwriter fire pump and three sets of motor-driven 15-in centrifugal pumps. Located next to Pigeon River.
Reservoir	Reinforced concrete construction with heavy timber roof, providing 300,000-gallons of water capacity for fire protection. Reservoir situated on hill north of plant at an elevation of 285 feet above mill.

Extract Plant

Barking Room	46x167: Two stories.
Regrinder Room	85x75: Two stories.
Chipping Room	50x143: Two stories.
Rough Leaching	86x134: Two stories.
Pulp Leaching	86x258: Two stories.
Evaporator Room	86x60: One story containing four large copper evaporators and various other apparatus which yields the tannin acid product of the extract department for shipping to customers in condensed form.
Boiler House	85x146: Two stories of brick, concrete, and steel construction, containing refuse boilers that burn bark, scrap wood, and leached chips. Boilers are thought to have been supplied and built by Edgar Boiler Company of New York City.

This was Thomson's pulp mill. As the spring of 1906 arrived, George Hardy was still working on the plant's design in his New York office. Just as soon as his drawings were completed, draftsmen jerked them off the drafting tables, made blueprint copies, and sent them as expeditiously as possible to Frank Gilbreth's construction team in Canton. Impatient construction bosses at the muddy work site then began the grueling struggle to drive forty miles of piling, construct massive concrete foundations, and erect the numerous sturdy brick buildings as fast as humanly possible.

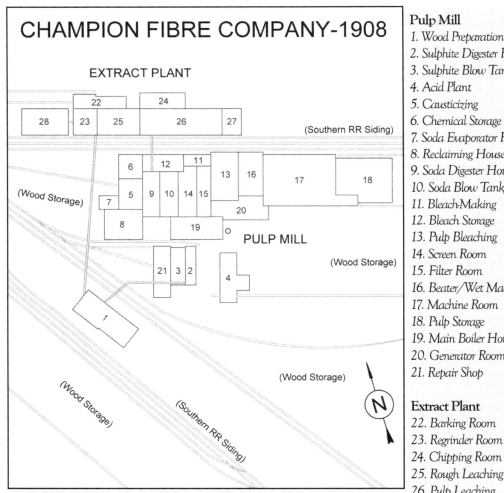

CHAMPION FIBRE COMPANY-1908

Pulp Mill
1. Wood Preparation
2. Sulphite Digester House
3. Sulphite Blow Tanks
4. Acid Plant
5. Causticizing
6. Chemical Storage
7. Soda Evaporator Room
8. Reclaiming House
9. Soda Digester House
10. Soda Blow Tank/Washing
11. Bleach-Making
12. Bleach Storage
13. Pulp Bleaching
14. Screen Room
15. Filter Room
16. Beater/Wet Machine Room
17. Machine Room
18. Pulp Storage
19. Main Boiler House
20. Generator Room
21. Repair Shop

Extract Plant
22. Barking Room
23. Regrinder Room
24. Chipping Room
25. Rough Leaching
26. Pulp Leaching
27. Evaporator House
28. Boiler House

(Plot plan of Champion Fibre Company's original buildings prepared by Hilary Cobb in cooperation with Haywood Community College.)

Pile-driving machines can be seen at work in the background of this photo, with their steam engines puffing and spewing black smoke. The timber construction in the foreground, which was referred to as "mill construction," is a good example of the floor framing used in many of the buildings. (from Sellars Collection)

Workers wearing bib overalls and felt hats use short-handled shovels to excavate for the building foundations. In this case, they appear to be trying to drain the rainwater out of the excavation. Note the piles that have been driven and the pile-driving machines working in the background. (from Sellars Collection)

Chapter 5
1906—Sea of Bottomless Mud

"Outside of the interest that attaches to this mammoth plant as a new Southern enterprise, there is a good story in the methods by which the contractor for the entire plant—the organization of which Mr. Frank B. Gilbreth of New York City is at the head—carried on the gigantic work in the heart of the North Carolina mountains, 800 miles from his executive offices."[65]

Such was the manner in which one contemporary report set out to describe the immense challenges faced by the Gilbreth Construction Company in building Peter Thomson's pulp mill and the construction methods that were used. The story recounted the struggles of the construction team in mid-1906, driving piles and pouring foundations in the "sea of bottomless mud" that Thomson had chosen for his mill site. It was said that the rains began in June and continued unremittingly until the cold winds of winter began to blow. "Pipe trenches and foundations would slump into nothingness over night, and have to be dug out anew the next day."[66, 67] But there is nothing new in such a sober analysis of a construction site. After all, construction is difficult work and always vulnerable to extreme weather conditions. Tough, hard-nosed construction men generally find ways to persevere and get things done.

Superintendent James Powers and his foremen were evidently possessed with the physical and mental fortitude required to meet the challenges at Canton. They pushed their five pile-driving crews all day long, every day, in efforts to keep the equipment steaming and hammering. As soon as piles were driven into the ground to the proper depths and the heavy rigs had advanced a safe distance, other teams of men moved in. Working in the mud much of the time, they used shovels and mattocks to excavate for the deep concrete foundations. After this slogging work was completed, the pile tops were cut off at the correct elevation and sawn boards were nailed into the shape of the desired concrete foundation. To provide more strength to the concrete, round iron reinforcing bars were placed inside this wooden mold. Then, countless hand-cart loads of concrete were poured into the formwork by the masons, completely filling the space and covering the pile tops and the reinforcing bars. That was how the building foundations were made, every last one of them. And after the concrete had hardened sufficiently, the forms were stripped away and the fresh concrete foundations backfilled with dirt. Then, and only then, could the brick masons move in and begin laying up the massive walls of the buildings.

It is easy to understand how the slow, tedious pile-driving activities impeded the early schedule. The concrete and brick work could not start before the piling was sunk. Gilbreth Construction (or simply Gilbreth), renowned for the speed with which it executed work, as well as for its novel methods, sought unique and efficient measures to drive some 8,000 to 10,000 piles into the ground faster. Early on, the bosses had concluded that more dependable and skilled men would have to be recruited to boost the production and get the work out of the mud. Consequently, by the summer of 1906 large gangs of men anxious for the opportunity to work were arriving by train daily. Many of these new workmen were recent immigrants from such unanticipated places as Italy, Bulgaria, and Ireland.

Gilbreth had designs on how to employ some of this new manpower to expedite the pile-driving work. Instead of using five crews made up of local men, it was decided to assemble a single local crew and four more teams of men from different countries or locations to man the five pile driving rigs. Then Gilbreth set the teams to work under equal conditions, challenging each to strive their hardest to drive the most piles in a single day. The team with the highest count received a colorful silk banner to fly at the top of their driver. It became a real source of pride for the crew flying the green flag of honor, because it showed every one of the many hundreds of workers on the job site who the champion pile-driving team was.

In fact, the daily contest became so competitive that Superintendent Powers himself began showing up an hour before starting time to insure that the crews did not get an early start on their rivals. Building up a head of steam, sliding the driver into position, and rigging a pile into place were little hedging maneuvers not beyond what a team might employ to get the jump on the others. Each morning, Superintendent Powers kept an eye out for these subtle irregularities and made sure the driving conditions were as equal as possible, before calling out in a loud voice, "Go!"[68]

Contemporary reports claim the work force numbered as many as eight hundred to a thousand men at one time during the building of Thomson's pulp mill. Unfortunately, there were few specialty boarding houses in Canton at the time.

Some workers were able to negotiate lodging arrangements with the town's citizens. The vast majority of the workers, however, were put up in barracks, shanties, and tents located around the construction site. Usually, these were segregated according to craft or nationality. Common unskilled laborers, masons, carpenters, ironworkers, mechanics, riggers, pipefitters, painters, and electricians shared separate living quarters—as did the foreign workmen.

A look to the west in the late summer of 1906 reveals both digester buildings rising in the background and the pulp storage warehouse nearing completion in the right foreground. No pulp wood is stored on the site yet, with the exception of timber piling and cut-off pile tops scattered all around. (from Sellars Collection)

The employees' living quarters were not the only things that were segregated on the construction grounds. Apparently, the commissary department, which played a vital role in keeping workers properly nourished, established more than one commissary on the site. According to at least one source, separate commissaries were set up for the higher class workmen such as the carpenters and masons.[69]

A gang of Bulgarians established their quarters near the river, where they built their own bake ovens shaped like beehives. These men of eastern European heritage were called "Rooshians" by the locals. Although considered slow and inefficient workers, they were dependable and would show up for work every day. The several hundred Italians who were brought in to boost the work force were also quartered on site. This was done in spite of the resistance of many workers and local citizens who apparently objected to the high number of foreigners being imported—especially Italians.[70]

An account from a Gilbreth employee revealed that the construction company was threatened with dire consequences if "dagos" were imported into the mountains. The contractor brought them in anyway, and after the first few "rough and tumble" encounters around the shanties, including a knife fight, things appear to have simmered down.[71] The Italians were as friendly as the rest, it was discovered, and they soon blended into the mix of rugged and skilled men erecting the huge buildings at Canton.[72, 73]

The photo shown on the preceding page is from late summer of 1906, and it shows the construction progress made up to that point. The brick walls of the sulphite and soda digester buildings have not yet reached the halfway height. Also, the sprawling two-story, pulp storage building is nearly topped out, although still windowless; and the machine room and pulp bleaching rooms are underway. Scaffold works surround the two digester buildings, including an access tower located at the center of each building's east wall. Stairs winding up these towers along with hoists provided the means by which workers could access the lofty heights and lift up their building materials.

Frank Gilbreth had boasted to Peter Thomson and touted in promotional ads his company's ability to speedily execute large brick jobs. The novel methods he customarily employed involved the application of his patented brick-laying tools as well as reusable pipe scaffolding. Many years after the construction work was completed at Canton and countless tons of pulp and paper had been produced, Thomson's son-in-law, Reuben B. Robertson, had more than a faint memory of Gilbreth's scientific brick-laying methods. It seems the brick masons, carpenters, and laborers who worked on the mill construction resisted their introduction to the Gilbreth methods. They obviously preferred the traditional wooden scaffolding, since Gilbreth's patented reusable metal scaffolding was conspicuously absent from the digester buildings and the other large buildings that were constructed. Photographs confirm this, and Robertson clearly recalled seeing huge piles of the expensive scaffolding stored in the scrap yard and rusting away, albeit earning the contractor's percentage profit.[74]

There was another thing Mr. Robertson would have keenly observed during the construction of his father-in-law's mill. Those brick buildings that George Hardy designed and Gilbreth's workers were laying up were exceptionally massive structures. Of course, the deep layer of river silt on the Canton site required extraordinary measures be taken to build them. As one instance, there were two continuous rows of timber piles running beneath each thick wall of the digester buildings. Hardy's foundation drawing spaced the piles two feet apart "on center," and specified that each one should support a load of at least seventeen tons. Consequently, these piles, which were about fifteen inches in diameter on the small end, were sunk twenty to thirty feet into the ground. Reinforced concrete pile caps and foundation walls were constructed over the piles to a height determined by a field engineer. On top of these foundations the brickwork was laid up.

Estimates given in various reports indicate that construction of Champion Fibre Company's mill in Canton required as many as 10,000,000 bricks from Alex A. Scott & Co. of Knoxville, Tennessee. Close to 160,000 bags of cement were also used.[75, 76]

The young man in charge of procuring the bricks and directing the extensive masonry works was Thomas Furness, all of twenty-four years old when the construction began. "Tommie" was an English brick mason who came to America via South Africa in 1903. In New York City, he learned about the work Gilbreth had contracted in Canton, North Carolina and applied for a job. Somehow, he wound up with more than just a brick mason's position. In 1906, he was named master mason and placed in complete charge of the bricklaying work at Canton.[77]

Ten million bricks—it is simply mind-boggling to contemplate such a number. Each and every brick had to be molded and fired, then loaded and shipped by rail from Knoxville to Canton. The circuitous train route passed through Morristown, Tennessee and then coursed along the twisting French Broad River through the mountain gaps to Asheville. Once the car loads of scorched red clay bricks finally arrived at Canton, every last one had to be off-loaded by hand from the rail cars, loaded onto wagons or handcarts, and hauled wherever they were needed on the site. Not uncommonly, the bricks and mortar would have to then be carried up scaffold steps, winched up scaffold towers, or pushed in handcarts over makeshift ramps to reach the masons working at dangerous heights to lay bricks as fast as they could.

Where in western North Carolina, or in the world for that matter, could enough brick masons be hired to lay 10,000,000 bricks to build the enormous buildings? As it turned out, Tommie Furness and James

Powers resorted to newspaper ads to find the skilled masons, including this solicitation in an Asheville paper:

> WANTED—50 *brick layers at once, to work on new mill buildings 18 miles from Asheville, N.C. on the Murphy Branch of the Southern R.R. Wages, 40 cents and up per hour. Long job there being ten million brick to lay. Apply to Frank H. [sic] Gilbreth, General Contractor, Canton, N.C.*[78]

Another amazing consideration associated with laying 10,000,000 bricks in the time it took to construct the Champion Fibre plant is the productivity achieved by Furness's brick mason crews. A calculation that considers this immense quantity of bricks, Gilbreth's six-day work week, and the eighteen-months required to lay all of the bricks yields an incredible result. The brick masons would have had to lay more than twenty thousand bricks every day! And just think, that was without the use of Frank Gilbreth's patented scaffolding and bricklaying tools.

It is very possible that Tommie Furness was also responsible for all of the concrete work. If so, he would have helmed Gilbreth's concrete manufacturing process. Of course this operation required plenty of gravel and sand, and both of these crucial raw materials were found on site. Gravel was quarried near the Pigeon River and sand was dredged directly from the river bottom.[79] After being hauled to separate hoppers and screened, the clean sand and properly sized rocks were then teamed to a large concrete mixer, which was also located on site (photo on page 53).

The mixing assembly, which was mounted directly over a timber containment bin, involved a cast iron rotating cylinder driven by a portable steam engine. Men fed sand, gravel, and cement directly into this mixing cylinder using a bucket elevator. It took only a few minutes of thoroughly mixing these ingredients with carefully measured quantities of water to manufacture concrete. The wooden bin below the rotating mixer held the concrete for only short periods of time, until it could be loaded into wagons or hand carts. Great care was taken during this entire process to insure that the concrete would cure to the specified strength, and that it was made to a lava-like consistency that allowed it to be transported, poured, and easily worked into the wooden forms.

Gilbreth's concrete manufacturing operation played an essential role in the construction of Thomson's pulp mill. It surely operated non-stop during the daylight hours, as the quarry and sand-dredging teams, concrete mixer operators, and delivery crews labored to supply fresh mortar and concrete to the masons working all across the vast construction site. Obviously, the building foundations were not the only structures to be built of reinforced concrete. Poured ground floor slabs, elevated floors, and fireproof roofs—such as those used in the two boiler houses—were specified by George Hardy's drawings. The acid and bleach-making buildings, and a few others, were built entirely

The Gilbreth Company's concrete manufacturing plant and its operator appear to be ready for another customer. Standing on a platform at the level where the discharge chute stop boards are located, a man is obviously waiting for the next empty wagon to roll up. As soon as the wagon arrives and is parked under him, he will pull out one or more stop boards and fill it up with concrete. The gravel and sand for the concrete mixture were mined from a quarry and the Pigeon River located nearby. These crucial materials along with cement were conveyed up to the mixer by the bucket elevator that extends from ground level to the mixer on top of the bin. At the right, a man who can barely be seen is working with a shovel and loading the bucket elevator. To the left of the huge timber containment bin is the portable steam engine which drove the rotating mixer assembly on top and the conveyor. A man standing next to the engine appears to be ready to make mechanical adjustments or stoke the boiler fire with scrap boards when necessary. (from Sellars Collection)

with concrete walls; and throughout the mill many tanks, bunkers, troughs, and hundreds of equipment foundations and bases were made of reinforced concrete. Without concrete, it would have been unfeasible to construct such an enormous, sophisticated pulp mill at the Canton construction site.

Two surviving photos taken during the winter of 1906–1907 confirm the remarkable progress made in less than a year's time. In the photo presented on the following pages, scaffolding still cloaks almost every building on the construction site. Although the sulphite digester building's roof is nicely topped out with a monitor, work has yet to begin on the soda digester building roof. This view is toward the southeast and it shows that the extract plant's various process buildings have been started, and are fairly well advanced. The exception being the plant's refuse boiler house. Wood piling scattered on the ground where it will eventually go up is probably a good indication that a pile-driving team will be showing up soon.

Another photo taken a couple of weeks later (page 57) reveals a wintry scene of snow blanketing the western mountains in the background and the roof tops of the mammoth factory buildings. Where once a sea of bottomless mud oozed, the ground is now frozen and covered with partially constructed buildings, construction materials, shacks, and a light dusting of snow. The sulphite digester building's recently finished roof and monitor can easily be spotted, while the soda digester house is shrouded in scaffolding with the roofing work still underway.

The Canton construction site was beginning to take shape in the last months of 1906 and was looking more and more like the mill Peter Thomson had envisioned. Mighty buildings had emerged from the ground and things seemed to be going well for the wealthy industrialist. However, in December of 1906, an extraordinary event dramatically altered most everyone's perception. Through the United Savings Bank & Trust Company of Cincinnati, Thomson publicized in a newspaper an offering of one million dollars of preferred stock of the Champion Fibre Company of Hamilton, Ohio. The letter as shown on page 56 gives further

In this early 1907 view, most of the mill's buildings appear to be behind scaffolding, including both digester houses. The extract plant boiler house, which will go up where the window frames and building materials are being staged in the foreground to the right, has not been started yet. However, there are timber piles lying scattered over the ground waiting for the pile-driving rig to be skidded over. (from Sellars Collection)

Hamilton, Ohio, November 19, 1906.

I beg to state that this company is incorporated under the laws of the State of Ohio, and the officers and the organization of the company are practically the same as the Champion Coated Paper Company.

The capital of the company is $2,000,000, divided as follows:
Preferred Stock...............................$1,000,000
Common Stock...............................$1,000,000

The Preferred is a 6% Cumulative Stock, and is non-taxable in the State of Ohio, and constitutes a first lien on all the property and assets of the company, and no prior lien can be created except by a three-fourths vote of the Preferred Shareholders.

The mills of the Champion Fibre Company, now approaching completion, are located at Canton, N.C., where the company owns 70 square miles of virgin woodland, and the buildings cover an area of nearly 15 acres, and are constructed of brick, steel, and cement, forming the largest combined sulphite and soda fibre plant in the world. The entire actual investment in the mills and real estate is over $2,500,000.

Under a ten years contract this company's entire output of sulphite and soda fibre, amounting to 200 tons daily, with a minimum value of $3,000,000 yearly, will be purchased by the Champion Coated Paper Company at the market price, and used by them at their paper and coating mill at Hamilton, Ohio, which plant is now being doubled in size for that purpose, and to meet the increased demand for its product.

The Net Annual Earnings of the Champion Fibre Company will be more than five times the amount necessary to pay the dividends of the Preferred Stock.

Very Truly Yours,
Peter G. Thomson, President. [80]

A November, 1906 public offering of preferred stock in the Champion Fibre Company was the means by which Peter G. Thomson raised much-needed cash to finance his Canton pulp mill enterprise.

A winter storm in early 1907 has left a light accumulation of snow across the construction site. The digester buildings stand out in naked contrast with the distant white-capped mountains. On the left, the sulphite digester house is topped out and the scaffolding has been removed, exposing the brickwork and many window openings in the east wall. Next to it is the soda digester house with roofing work still in progress. To the far right, the pulp warehouse building looks to be complete. (from Sellars Collection)

particulars accompanying the offer.

Undoubtedly, the decision to sell stock in his Champion Fibre Company was one of necessity for Peter Thomson. He relinquished complete ownership and control of the company for a reason: he needed the money. Given the large expenditures to fund the Canton mill's exorbitant construction costs and the expense of doubling the output of the Hamilton mill, Mr. Thomson was strapped for cash. Additionally, construction of Laurel Court, his grand estate near Cincinnati, was ongoing and there were tremendous debts associated with building and furnishing such a magnificent mansion. An infusion of cash from the stock offering was apparently the best option he had at the time.

However, the financial angst would not be eased with this action. Thomson wrote in the letter to potential stockholders that construction of the Champion Fibre Company was "approaching completion." Unbeknownst to him, it would be more than a year before he would receive any North Carolina pulp at his Ohio factory. Not only that, the nation was headed toward an economic crisis that would test his physical health and his wherewithal to complete the new pulp mill and extract plant.

Photos from 1906

At about the time of the construction of Thomson's pulp mill, this was the view of Canton from the top of the Southern Railway's "deep cut." The railroad depot can be seen in the center foreground next to the parked railcar. Champion's pulp mill will be constructed on the property to the right of the railroad tracks, beyond the embankment and out of sight in this view. The Southern's tracks are aimed westward across the Pigeon River directly at the Penland-Wells house in the distance. In the late 1970's, the house was demolished to make way for the current Canton Post Office. (from Sellars Collection)

In the spring of 1906, piling was being pounded into the muddy ground as fast as Gilbreth Company's five pile-driving rigs pictured in this photo could work. (from Sellars Collection)

Posing in front of their tent (or office) are the surveyors who ran the lines for the proposed pulpwood water flume and Pigeon River Railway routes. They also surveyed the pulp mill construction site and laid out the horizontal and elevation controls for the mill construction work. The young man on the left is Tommie Remson, and next to him is the Civil War veteran, Captain William H. Hargrove. (from Canton Area Historical Museum)

The Gilbreth and Champion construction bosses are checking out the pile-driving and foundation work on the north side of the site where the extract plant is being built. It is likely that James Powers and Thomas Marr are amongst them.

These workers are busy building a ramp for the concrete hand carts to run across. In the left background sunlight is reflecting off a large building that is probably a barracks and commissary. (from Sellars Collection)

This is a view to the southwest in late summer or fall of 1906, showing both digester houses under construction in the right background. The pulp mill's machine room and pulp storage warehouse on the left are under construction and well along. A temporary wood frame building in the foreground is most likely a barracks for the workers. Note in the distant background the original iron-truss railroad bridge spanning the Pigeon River and the prominent Penland-Wells house in the far distance. (from Sellars Collection)

A late summer view to the west in 1906 shows buildings and scaffolding on the rise. The sulphite digester building is on the left, and the pulp machine room and pulp storage warehouse appear in the right foreground. The soda digester building can just barely be made out behind the concrete walls of the filter and screen rooms, but its scaffold tower can clearly be seen. (from Sellars Collection)

This photo of the interior of one of the mill buildings shows columns, floor beams, flooring, and overhead beams constructed out of timber. Otherwise known as "mill construction," it was a common way of building when significant machinery loads were not anticipated or corrosion from wet or chemical environments was a concern. One of the first buildings to be completed was the pulp storage warehouse and this could possibly be it. As can be seen, new equipment is already being stored in it. (from Sellars Collection)

This long lineup of brick buildings under construction in late 1906 or early 1907 is associated with the tannin extract plant. Scaffolding cloaks the south walls, windows have been blocked-out with timber framing, and many busy masons can be seen laying up bricks on the east wall in the foreground. (from Sellars Collection)

In late 1906 or early 1907, the 122-ft high sulphite digester house was topped out with its monitor roof, but the scaffolding was still in place. Note at the bottom of the photo stacks of wooden window frames ready to be inserted into the brick walls, a railroad sidetrack, tops of piles sticking out of the ground, and an excavation for a drainage tile. (from Sellars Collection)

In late 1906 or early 1907, this view looking to the northeast shows that the pulp machine room (with skylights) and the pulp storage building at the far right are almost complete.

At the bottom of the photo, a pile-driving rig is working in the area where the generator room is going up. (from Sellars Collection)

This pile-driver's heavy iron weight is falling as workmen steady a pile being pounded into the ground. (from Sellars Collection)

Chapter 6
Boom Town

The Town of Canton was growing as fast as Peter Thomson's factory buildings were rising on the north side of the Southern's railroad tracks. In April 1907, the population had expanded from 350 inhabitants the previous year to 1,680 full-time citizens—not including boarding and transient construction workers. One newspaper release at about this time claimed that thirty-eight new residences had already been built in Canton since the beginning of the year, and seven new store buildings had gone up.[81] Another source revealed that by mid-year there was "fully one house complete being built each day in Canton," and these were rented "before it was begun to be constructed."[82] It is likely that many of these new rental properties were the small company houses being built for the fibre mill's workers in a village appropriately named "Fibreville." This community was located about a half-mile downstream and across the river from Thomson's pulp mill, on a tract of land that had been extremely difficult to acquire.

As soon as Thomson's mill management team–Jim Harris, Oma Carr, Charles Bryant, and a man named Thomas Marr— had arrived in Canton in late 1905 and early 1906, they threw themselves into the operational planning as well as the oversight of Gilbreth Construction Company's work. It was not long, however, before they realized that more land was needed. There was barely sufficient space on the east side of the Pigeon River to erect the mill buildings and develop an expansive pulpwood storage yard with side tracks. Certainly, the permanent housing necessary for the mill employees and their families could not be built on the mill site. Upon learning of this latest assessment, Peter Thomson instructed George Smathers to look into acquiring more land on the west side of the Pigeon River, forthwith.

Smathers and his boss had previously made an unsuccessful attempt to purchase the piece of bottomland across the river immediately opposite the mill. The price had been too high at the time; moreover, Thomson had not thought the land to be of extreme value for his enterprise. Now that things could be viewed in a different light, Mr. Smathers immediately began negotiations with a lawyer representing the Penland heirs who owned the land. The attorney promptly informed Smathers that he would not recommend a sale for less than two hundred dollars an acre, more than twice the price Thomson had paid for the acreage where his mill was under construction. Additionally, Smathers learned that one of the Penland heirs was mentally ill and under legal guardianship. After advising Mr. Thomson of the situation and that a lengthy court proceeding would be necessary to purchase the Penland family land, Smathers was instructed to turn his attention to another large tract adjacent to and downstream of the Penland property.

Commonly known as the "Jincie Patton tract," this fifty-five acre or so plot of land, and considerably more property besides, was owned by Mary Ann Luther Patton, the widow of James McConnell Patton.[83] Attorney Smathers wrote in great length in his unpublished memoirs about the extraordinary negotiations that took place with Mrs. Patton, while trying to persuade her to sell the land. He wrote that Montgomery Smith was the first to approach her on Thomson's behalf. Having previously heard from someone that Smith could hypnotize people, the widow Patton kept a fair distance from him and, as might be expected, Smith gained no ground in his attempt to win her approval. However, Mrs. Patton learned from Smith that George Smathers was one of Peter Thomson's lawyers, and she requested a conference with this man whom she had once taught in grade school.

"Well, George Henry, I sent for you for the reason that I believed you to be honest and would tell the truth about matters, or at least I used to think you were honest, but did not know so well about it since you had got to be a lawyer." That was how Mrs. Patton opened the first meeting with Smathers. She remarked that she was disdainful of lawyers and of the Canton political machine that included a Mr. Hampton, Mr. Mease, and Mr. Scott. Not only that, she was very keen to know what effect the fumes from the mill would have on her timber, and whether or not the pollution in the water would poison her stock. Smathers was not caught totally off guard, having studied up on these issues, and he did his best to address Mrs. Patton's concerns.

He informed her that his previous investigations into these very matters proved that the fumes from the pulp mill would not destroy or impair the surrounding trees and forests. And as to water pollution, the best he could tell was that the stock would not want to drink the water; but, if they did, it would not poison them. However, he believed that most of the fish might be killed. To this last point, Mrs. Patton surprisingly replied that she did not consider the fish to be of much value to her. There was plenty of clear running water on her large property holdings that the stock could drink. Besides, the fish only provided a distraction for her shiftless tenants, who would rather fish in the spring and summer than work the crops on her land.

Mrs. Patton also inquired as to how she would benefit from the building of the pulp mill located literally next door to her land. To this Smathers replied that the value of her land obviously would increase. When asked if her land would become

more productive, he confessed that he was not sure about that. Unmoved, Mrs. Patton allowed she wanted to leave her land to her children and grandchildren, and an increase in property value would only give the Canton political machine another excuse for increasing her property taxes—and she did not want that!

A discussion followed over the price of the Jincie Patton tract. Smathers told Mrs. Patton that Peter Thomson was prepared to pay as much as one hundred dollars per acre for the property; that is, if she would sign an agreement releasing Thomson of damages on account of the pollution of the water of the Pigeon River. He further argued that she would realize much more out of the interest on the money than she would get out of renting it to lazy tenants. After a lengthy exchange of views along these lines, Mrs. Patton at last suggested to her former student that it was time for her to meet the "Big Man," meaning Mr. Thomson himself. She wanted to talk things over with him and see if it might be possible to come to an agreement on the terms of a sale. Widow Patton was adamant, however, that she would have no part of a formal agreement releasing Mr. Thomson from damages caused from the pollution of the river by his pulp mill.

Not long after that, Mr. Peter Thomson and his wife Laura steamed into Canton on the train, hired a team at the local livery, and drove out to see Mrs. Patton. George Smathers accompanied them, and along the way the attorney prepared the

Thomsons for the conference. He later wrote that Mrs. Laura Thomson struck him as being "a lady of fine personality and most agreeable manners, and made friends with everybody with whom she came in contact, and immediately after entering the house of Mrs. Patton she made friends with Mrs. Patton and aided in getting Mrs. Patton in a good mood."

Following an exchange of awkward introductions and niceties, Peter Thomson proceeded to initiate the formal discussion by stating his purpose and the important matters he wanted to talk about that afternoon. However, Mrs. Patton was by no means going to be rushed. As maintained by Smathers, she wanted the "Big Man" to know how his agent, Mr. Smith, attempted to hypnotize her and get her property for nothing. After that grievance was aired, they got down to business in a more amicable manner, discussing terms and pricing for the Jincie Patton tract. In just a few days a deal was struck, where Mrs. Patton reportedly sold the land to Thomson for one hundred dollars per acre—half the price the Penlands were demanding for an adjacent tract.

Attorney Smathers recalled many years later that Peter Thomson had asked him while riding away from that first conference with Mrs. Patton, "Smathers, do you really think that old lady believes in hypnotism?" When Smathers affirmed his suspicion that the woman might actually harbor a fear of hypnosis, Thomson was stupefied. The astute and wealthy business magnate

could not reconcile that belief with Mrs. Patton's common sense in business matters. In fact, Thomson thought her to be "one of the smartest women he had ever talked to!"[84]

Interestingly, Haywood County's deed records reveal that the parcel of land sold by Mary Ann Patton to Peter G. Thomson in June, 1906, was actually sixty acres, or thereabouts—not the fifty-five acres so often stated by Smathers and other sources. The deed records also indicate she received four thousand dollars "delivered to her in hand" for the property, not quite the hundred dollars per acre that attorney Smathers remembered. But there could well have been other forms of compensation related to the transaction that went unrecorded. True to her word however, an agreement relieving Thomson of damages resulting from water pollution caused by his pulp mill was not reached.

It is very enlightening that at this early stage of the pulp mill's existence—before it had even been placed into operation—the local citizens were already informed and wary about the water and air pollution that might be created by Thomson's pulp mill. Their farsightedness actually preceded Peter Thomson's fantasy of building a pulp mill deep in the western North Carolina mountains. Back in 1901, Colonel Silas A. Jones of Waynesville had actually secured the passage of an act in the North Carolina General Assembly to encourage the building of pulp mills, paper mills, and tanneries in Haywood and Swain counties!

The act contained in Chapter 690 of the North Carolina Public Laws of 1901 can be summarized as follows:

Any corporation spending $100,000 or more in establishing a factory to convert wood into wood pulp for making paper and other products of pulp shall not be subject to any criminal prosecution for the pollution of any watercourse upon which factory or factories are located, and the measure of damages to the owners of lands over which the water flows from such factory or factories shall be confined to actual damages, to be ascertained as provided by law.

Although this law was very specifically written to benefit the counties of Haywood and Swain, the drawback for Smathers and Peter Thomson was that it applied only to the Pigeon River lands below the mouth of Jonathan's Creek, a small tributary located several miles downstream from Canton. Not only could landowners between Canton and the mouth of Jonathan's Creek bring suit against Champion Fibre Company for property damages deriving from water pollution caused by the mill, but the company could also be liable for criminal prosecution. Smathers and Colonel Jones had previously attempted to use this shortcoming in the law as leverage when arguing for the selection of sites other than Canton to build Thomson's pulp mill. However, Peter Thomson's infatuation with his spruce timber on the Pigeon River

headlands and Smith's impossible flume had moved him to brush aside even this legal vulnerability.

Thomson's recourse to the dilemma was to have attorney Smathers secure agreements from the landowners along the Pigeon River between Canton and Jonathan's Creek, releasing himself, his heirs, and assigns from damages on account of pollution of the river. For the most part, Mr. Smathers was successful, with at least one exception being the case of Mrs. Mary Ann Patton, who refused to sign such an agreement.[85]

Once the real estate transaction with the widow Patton was concluded and while the environmental legal complexities were being addressed, construction of the village that became known as Fibreville was begun on the Jincie Patton tract. The man put in charge of supervising construction of the company houses in Fibreville was Thomas Marr. He had previously worked at Buena Vista Extract Works in Virginia with Oma Carr, who likely recruited Marr to come to Canton. Marr was described in one account as looking like an ordinary laborer but was "a man of culture, high intelligence, and unusual executive ability." He must have had an outstanding mechanical mind. After graduating from the Virginia Polytechnic Institute with an engineering degree, Marr worked in railroad shops and later installed the machinery at the Buena Vista extract plant.[86] Upon his arrival in Canton on November 1, 1905, this highly competent engineer was forty-one years old, experienced, and ready for any responsibility he might be assigned. So while Gilbreth was constructing the pulp mill and tannin extract plant structures, Thomas Marr was given the important job of building company houses.

In all likelihood, actual construction of the houses at Fibreville did not start until mid-1906, when the title to the Patton property actually passed to Peter Thomson.

Thomas Marr came to Canton in 1905 and was responsible for constructing the employee houses in the village of Fibreville. As a Champion Fibre Company supervisor, he also oversaw Gilbreth Construction's work building the tannin extract plant. Marr later became the superintendent of that plant. (from Sellars Collection)

A road, which later became the Main Street of Fibreville, was laid out parallel to the Pigeon River. Off of this principal road, four additional cross roads—A, B, C, and D—were graded, and these stretched across the narrow bottom, ending rather abruptly at the base of a steep hill. Along the main avenue and the cross streets, Thomas Marr and his teams of workers and mules began constructing little houses at a furious pace.

The old photograph on the next page shows that by early 1907, many company houses had been completed or were under construction in Fibreville. Marr utilized the same architectural template over and over again, building identical four-room structures, each of them two rooms wide and two deep. These small frame cottages were set on brick piers with their gable ends oriented toward the street. Every one of them was covered in gray-painted weatherboarding and had wood-shingle roofs with covered front porches. A small detached privy attended each residence and common woodsheds were shared by adjoining neighbors. It is believed there were originally about forty homes in Fibreville, all completed and occupied by up to "three hundred to four hundred people" during the latter phase of the mill's construction.[87]

Canton was being called western North Carolina's boom town, and in the first quarter of 1907 alone seven new store buildings had gone up along with many residences. A new bank had opened its doors

Company houses in the village of Fibreville are in various stages of construction. The ones furthest away appear to be complete, and smoke can be detected rising from at least one chimney. Based on the construction status of the mill's digester buildings in the distance, the timeframe is early 1907. (from Canton Area Historical Museum)

in late 1906, and was chartered under the name Champion Bank of Canton. In addition to Peter G. Thomson, several prominent Haywood County men became founding members. These included G.W. Maslin of Waynesville, and Canton was represented by William J. (Dick) Hampton, Charles T. (Charley) Wells, Joseph Nelson (Nelse) Mease, James H. Mease, H. Arthur Osborne, and Oscar Mears Hampton.[88] In the absence of another well-funded finan-

cial institution, the opening of this bank in Canton was demanded by the immense sums of money being paid out by the Champion Fibre Company to innumerable suppliers of labor, materials, rail shipments, and machinery.

The company required a local bank to secure its money and pay out cash to the holders of checks issued by Secretary-Treasurer Charles Bryant. Citizens of Canton—growing in numbers and wealth each and every day—also needed a bank to guard their precious earnings and savings. Almost overnight, the term "payday" became one of unprecedented importance, as hundreds of construction workers and a growing number of Champion Fibre employees paraded over to the bank to deposit their well-earned cash or paychecks. Of course, the merchants and storekeepers—men such as Dick Hampton, Nelse Mease, and Charley Wells—were careful to display their wares to greatest advantage, in order that they might lighten the pockets of the hard-working men and their families.

Certainly, this was nothing new or untoward. It was actually a sign of the boom town economy being born in Canton at the time. The bustling market was dependent on several things including Peter Thomson's providing good jobs with fair pay, construction and factory workers' labors rewarded with living wages, and merchants exchanging valuable goods and services for the workers' earnings. Canton's boom town economy in the years to come would realize vigorous growth and prosperity beyond anyone's wildest dreams.

Two of the Champion Bank's charter members were Big Five men who had played prominent roles back in 1905 enticing Peter Thomson to build his pulp mill in Canton. Not only did Dick Hampton and Nelse Mease sell parcels of land to Thomson on which he was building his plant, but they had also promised to deliver substantial tax breaks for his enterprise, per attorney George Smathers' account. Mr. Thomson had assured the Big Five that if they carried out their promises, he would not put up a commissary for the mill workers, as was usual with such a large manufacturing facility. Canton's merchants could then compete for the Champion employees' business. Now, after a couple of years and more than a million dollars invested across the railroad tracks, and with the towering buildings in plain view, the Canton men's memories apparently failed them.

In 1907, the tax assessor for Beaverdam Township, which encompassed the Town of Canton and the site of Thomson's pulp mill, established a valuation of $750,000 for the structures and machinery under construction and installation at the Champion Fibre Company. Both Peter Thomson and his attorney, George Smathers, were astounded that the valuation could be so high, especially since most of the buildings were still incomplete and the machinery was not in operation. When challenged by George Smathers, the assessor claimed it to be a fair evaluation since he had researched and determined that the Champion Fibre Company had spent at least this sum on lands, construction, and machinery received up to that point.

Smathers later remembered that their appeals for help to Dick Hampton, Mayor Nelse Mease, and the others who represented the Big Five fell on deaf ears. Instead, they defended the high valuation and reminded Smathers that the town had recently taken on $65,000 of bonded indebtedness to

fund improvements to the town's infrastructure. Work was either being planned or underway for a new water works and sewage system,
extensive grading and paving of streets, electric
street lights, and construction of a new public
school.[89] It was their opinion that all of this was
mostly for the benefit of Mr. Thomson and his
mill employees, and they felt he should pay a
substantial share of taxes for the town.

Peter Thomson surely trembled in fury as he
wrote to Smathers that the big men of Canton
had not carried out their promises, and he felt
no obligation to delay establishing a commissary at the plant. When the Big Five received
word of this, they retrenched, agreeing to do
everything in their power to effect a reduction
in the valuation of the mill's property from the
Board of Equalization. As a result of a formal
hearing, the Board reduced Champion's valuation to $500,000. George Smathers and Peter
Thomson were still not satisfied, and further
negotiations ensued.

In the end, the board would not accept
the $150,000 valuation that Champion Fibre
proposed, but they did agree to carry over the
same property valuation of $500,000 for the
coming year.[90] Smathers reflected on these
tax disputes years later and stated that he
saw no evidence that the Big Five had ever
intervened to help Peter Thomson and the
Champion Fibre Company. They simply "lay
down on the job."[91] Obviously, Mr. Smathers
was only referring to the tax troubles. He could
not have forgotten that both Dick Hampton
and Nelse Mease had sold properties at a fair
price to Peter Thomson, on which he had built
his pulp mill.

This pile-driver operator stopped working to allow the photographer to take his picture. The man's identity is unknown, but he is wearing a tie and certainly has the looks of a foreign workman. Perhaps he is one of the many Italians who helped build the Champion Fibre Company. (from Sellars Collection)

Workers Photographs

Frank Bunker Gilbreth of New York City was the head of Gilbreth Construction Company. The contractor was renowned for performing work on a "cost-plus-fixed sum" basis. However, for some reason, Peter Thomson entered into a contract with Gilbreth that could best be described as a "cost-plus-percentage" arrangement. That is, the contractor's fee was a pre-determined percentage of the actual cost of the construction work. It was an agreement that proved to be very costly to the Champion Fibre Company. (Courtesy of Purdue University Libraries, Karnes Archives and Special Collections)

This pile-driving rig's fire is still lit and its boiler is steaming while the crew takes a break to have their picture taken. It can easily be seen here how the heavy equipment was skidded on rolling logs and positioned precisely before driving each timber pile into the ground. (from Canton Area Historical Museum)

A crew of Champion Fibre employees takes a few minutes off to have their image taken in the original main boiler house. They are surrounded by twenty Heine boilers and the coal bin is located high over their heads. (from Canton Area Historical Museum)

Gilbreth Construction's supervisors are shown here posing in front of their construction office. Superintendent James F. Powers is the third man from the left. (from Canton Area Historical Museum)

These employees are holding the tools of their trade, as they stare stoically toward a focal point to the side of the camera. Although it is difficult to make out in the photo, a prankster is peeping through a hole in the wall behind the men and doing his best to distract them. (from Sellars Collection)

Mule teams driven by African-American teamsters are shown in this photo pulling wagon loads of materials and equipment across the construction site. (from Sellars Collection)

The management meetings held at lunch time each day were called the "Dinner Crowd" meetings. At one such meeting the Champion Fibre Company bosses paused to have their photo taken. They are as follows: (seated left to right) C.E. Smith, F.W Winchester, C.S. Badgett, W.J. Dial, "Uncle" Joe Clark, Reuben B. Robertson, Sr., Thomas Marr, Charles S. Bryant, W.R. Chute, R.J. Sprang, Wm. Battison, and W.E Roberts; (standing left to right) D.V. Blaney, George M. Trostel, A.D. Wood, and G.W. Phillips. (from Sellars Collection)

Construction workmen captured in this photo (ethnicity unknown) appear to be having a gay old time outside of their barracks. Their attentions are drawn to the man in overalls with his back to the camera. Wish we could see what musical instrument he was playing—or maybe he was only dancing. (from Sellars Collection)

A Champion Fibre Company boss (possibly Thomas Marr) is surrounded by a crew of employees. A couple of men have shed their headwear, and one appears to be gripping a hammer. (from Sellars Collection)

A mother and her litter wait patiently outside the barracks for their master to come home from a hard day's work at the pulp mill. (from Sellars Collection)

A young boy poses in a very precarious position, standing barefooted on a railroad track and holding his daddy's heavy axe. (from Sellars Collection)

A tall timber gin pole installed in the center of the building is being used to lift heavy structural steel roof trusses into place. (from Sellars Collection)

Chapter 7
1907—A Challenging Year

When the last snow had melted from the high roofs of the digester buildings in early 1907, work at Thomson's pulp mill was advancing at a heightened pace. Wood scaffolding shrouded the final brick buildings to go up, including the two boiler houses, generator room, and the wood preparation buildings. Smoke spewed high into the air from the stacks of red-hot steam engines powering equipment in the saw mill, construction shops, and river pump house. The concrete mixing plant and several pile drivers emitted their own black mushroom clouds, a good indication that concrete pours were continuing and the piling was still being pounded into the ground. The Southern Railroad's locomotive was charging around the site, delivering equipment and supplies wherever needed and picking up empty cars. On the east side, the railroad company's excavation work lowering the cut was still underway, and the huge steam shovel being employed in that business was contributing its fair share of noise and commotion to the scene. But that was not all that could be spotted by the discerning eye.

Staged across the site among the completed and nearly completed brick buildings were all sorts of devices made from iron and steel. There were huge vessels with rounded dome ends, neatly stacked lengths of pipe, structural fabrications, cylindrical tanks, and mechanical equipment of every description. Mechanics, iron workers, and rigging crews were at work using various methods and means to move, lift, and install the equipment just where George Hardy's drawings specified and where Gilbreth's and Champion's superintendents said to put it. Rail car after rail car arriving at Canton's depot was diverted onto the mill site where they could be off-loaded as quickly as possible. The empty cars were moved out to make room for ones loaded with boiler assemblies, fans, conveyors, pumps, motors, and every sort of pulping machinery needed to convert wood chips into pulp in the most labor-saving manner.

Carpenters and masons were hurrying to finish their work in order to make way for men with other skills to install mechanical equipment designed to cut, chip, mix, cook, clean, screen, drain, beat, heat, cool, dry, and convey the many forms of liquids, solids, and air encompassed in the pulp production process. Once the equipment was set in exactly the place that Oma Carr, Thomas Marr, Jim Harris, Joe Clark, Carl Jentz and the other Champion bosses wanted it, then representatives of the equipment suppliers directed workmen of all trades as they labored to prepare the machinery for start-up.

All of the building trades were working at once across the mill construction site as the months of 1907 quickly came and passed. In addition to the equipment installation activities, timber piling continued to be driven deep into the ground by the different national teams. Carpenters and joiners were still absolutely indispensable: building concrete formwork and erecting scaffolding, ramps, and platforms; fabricating and putting up timber posts, beams, flooring, and roofing; and installing hundreds of doors, windows, and skylights. Tommie Furness's masons carried on with manufacturing and pouring concrete, as well as doing their upmost to lay twenty thousand bricks each and every day. Lest it be forgotten, Thomas Marr's workmen were hurrying as fast as possible to put up the company's employee houses at Fibreville and other places where there was some property to spare. The construction pace was furious, as everyone strived to complete their work so Peter Thomson's pulp mill could begin production to meet the supply demands of the Hamilton, Ohio coated paper mill.

One report stated that a thousand car loads of machinery would be received at Canton and installed before the mammoth fibre plant began operations. Another revealed that a single equipment contract worth $300,000 was the largest individual contract ever let in western North Carolina. In May 1907, Secretary-Treasurer Charles Bryant thought the construction work was advancing well and predicted the pulp mill and tannin extract plant would begin production in October—or November at the latest. Champion and Gilbreth Construction were then employing six hundred to seven hundred workers of all types to get this done, at a weekly-payroll expenditure of $7,000 to $8,000. Mr. Bryant further added that a like amount was being expended every week for the freight bills. All totaled, including the building materials, machinery, freight, employee payroll, and Hardy's and Gilbreth's fees, the cost of building Thomson's pulp mill was approaching $2,250,000.[92, 93]

A staggering sum this was, and it partially explained why Peter Thomson began selling stock in the Champion Fibre Company. There were also the previously-mentioned tax troubles that reared up in mid-1907. But enormous outlays of money and tax obligations were not the only things that plagued Thomson's great enterprise as construction raced forward in 1907. On the very first day of the year, a knife fight broke out among the Italians at their quarters on the construction site. It was described as "a serious stabbing affray," a description that apparently was not understated. Five or six men were involved in the fight, with three of them receiving life-threatening injuries. Canton's police officers arrested three individuals, but the guiltiest of the bunch, according to eye-witness accounts, was not apprehended. He may even have made his way back to Italy.[94]

Photographs taken at the beginning of spring offer ample evidence of the progression of the work all across the site. Mostly unseen in these photos are the multitudes of tradesmen laboring furiously to build the mill—some of them climbing to

elevated perches to pour concrete, lay bricks, erect wood and steel structures, and rig large pieces of equipment—all in the most dangerous of circumstances. It should not be surprising that many men were seriously injured and even killed in the advancement of Thomson's mill. Newspaper accounts throughout the entire construction period offer details of numerous gruesome accidents.

In one unfortunate incident, a man erecting steel girders in one of the plant's buildings was maimed when the hoisting system broke and a mass of steel fell on the platform where he stood. The ironworker did not die, but on account of his badly scarred face and a stiff leg, he sued Gilbreth Construction and Champion Fibre for an unknown sum in damages, charging carelessness and negligence on their part.[95]

In yet another horrific case, a carpenter fell from a height of thirty feet onto a concrete floor, severely crushing most of the bones in his face. He also sustained a compound fracture to his left thigh. Luckily, he too survived. Two other carpenters were not so fortunate. A brick wall that suddenly collapsed buried them under tons of brick and mortar.[96]

Not only was the construction work dangerous, it was hard, grueling, and tiresome. Toughness of mind and body was a requisite for employment, as the workmen expended enormous energy plying their skills and the force of their bodies over the course of long ten-hour work days. Perhaps it was inevitable that after laboring for an entire year under ten-hour work-day rules the carpenters finally walked out on Gilbreth Construction and the

On Labor Day, 1907, a long procession made up of Champion Fibre Company dignitaries, the 1st Regiment Band of Asheville, and Champion and Gilbreth Construction employees paraded through Canton, making its way to the company "baseball grounds." Once there, the parade participants lined up for a ceremonial review and to have this remarkable photo made.

Champion Fibre Company. Around one hundred and fifty men put up this united front, demanding that the work day be reduced to nine hours for the same pay—an average of $2.00 per day.[97, 98, 99]

It may not come as a surprise to learn that several carpenters' unions across the southeast instigated walkouts over similar grievances at about the same time. It was likely a coordinated action, and at Canton the work was tied up for a couple of days until Gilbreth and Champion Fibre settled the issue and put the men back to work. Champion insisted that the ten-hour days be continued at the same pay rate, but offered to compensate the workers time-and-a-half for the last hour on Monday through Friday and the last two hours on Saturday.[100] It is believed that this offer, or something very similar, was the basis of the settlement.

The Champion Fibre employees, Gilbreth Construction workers, and citizens of the Town of Canton put aside all grievances and other concerns long enough to enjoy a couple of grand celebrations in 1907. In honor of the country's Independence Day on July 4th, there were many sporting events which started at nine o'clock in the morning on the Champion Fibre Company's grounds.

Each trade, such as the masons, carpenters, and ironworkers, wore different uniforms. For example, the electricians were dressed in "khaki uniforms with soft white hats and white ties." The parade was reported to have been "the grandest ever let loose in Canton." (from Sellars Collection)

These included a tug-of-war and races of every kind imaginable, such as a shoe race, fat-man's race, and banana race. Music was furnished by the Waynesville Band; and there was a baseball game between the electrical and construction departments, and another contest pitting Champion Fibre employees against Yandle Brothers Construction Company. Certainly, the day was not without fireworks, which got started just as darkness descended on the masses of excited yet worn-out spectators.[101]

Nonetheless, the Fourth-of-July holiday paled in comparison to the one held on September 2nd. A newspaper account touted that, "There has been the greatest crowd here [Canton] today that has ever assembled to witness the celebration of Labor Day." It was truly a grand affair and was said that the "country swain with his sweetheart, women with crying babies, fakers with all kinds of games, wrestling matches, baseball games, a parade, and the hot weather contributed their part to the enjoyment of the day." By far, the grandest parade ever let loose in Canton proceeded down Main Street and over a dusty road toward the baseball grounds at the lower end of the Champion Fibre Company's property. When they finally reached those company grounds, approximately four hundred Champion and Gilbreth Construction employees in full uniform lined up for a review and to have their photograph made.

Silence and time must not obscure the organization and personages involved in this magnificent Labor Day parade. At the head were the mounted officers of the North Carolina Guard followed in a carriage by General Manager Jim Harris and a corps of Champion and Gilbreth supervisors including Thomas Judge, D.J. Kerr, J.S. Adams, Joe Clark, L.N. Fowler, and James F. Powers. Behind them, in another carriage, were Superintendent Carl Jentz of the Sulphite Mill and his family. The First Regiment Band of Asheville marched after these distinguished dignitaries, while at the same time rendering a splendid blend of music.

The long procession that followed included several groups of uniformed employees. These included the brick masons dressed in white uniforms, carpenters and joiners wearing blue trousers and white-striped jackets, electricians dressed in khaki uniforms with soft white hats and white ties, iron workers attired in blue overalls, pipefitters lavishly decked out as well, and, finally, painters bringing up the rear and wearing white uniforms. Mixed in with this entourage of tradesmen was a team and float of the Black-Clawson Company from Hamilton, Ohio, the supplier of huge steel paper rolls for the mill, and Chairman Eugene A. Hyde (chairman of the Labor Day Planning Committee) who was mounted on horseback.

After a ceremonial review of the long procession was held at the baseball grounds and a photograph taken, the races and other events began. A speedy Will Coman won the 100-yard dash competition, and the painters managed to whip the pipefitters in a tug-of-war battle. C.V. Cannon and Jack Overend took both the three-legged race and the wheelbarrow race, while Coman managed to prevail once again in the potato race. There was even a fat man's race, in which L. Drake edged out A. Case for the highest honor. Besides the racing events held on that special day, many young men participated in contests that tested their leaping athleticism. The broad jump champion was L.M. Clawson, and Joe Mann hurdled over a bar set at a height of four feet and six inches to capture the high jump title.

One Charles A. Mooney, an employee of the Champion Fibre Company and described as being a long slim fellow, hooked up in a wrestling match with the champion of Tennessee—a man by the name of Louis Winnick. Although Mooney made some clever escapes from getting his shoulders pinned against the mat and was much applauded by the large crowd, he was no match for his formidable opponent. Winnick bested him in two rounds that lasted almost forty minutes.

Certainly the day would not have been complete without a high-spirited baseball game, such as the one contested by Champion Fibre Company employees and Bryson City. Not only because Champion—or Canton—won the game, but for everything else including the victory, this was truly a

Yandle Brothers' workmen take a water break during excavation of a cut on the Pigeon River Railroad. They are holding sledge hammers and hand drills, which meant that yet another dynamite blast was imminent. The young water boy's bare feet must have been as tough as these men. (from Gerald Ledford collection)

great day in the history of Canton and one not soon forgotten. Still, just as sure as the sun rose the following Tuesday morning, the tradesmen discarded their showy uniforms, donned their work attire, and hefted their tools to begin another long hard day at Thomson's pulp mill.[102, 103, 104]

Up the Pigeon River a ways, Yandle Brothers was pushing with all possible speed the construction work on the Pigeon River Railway's road from Canton to Sunburst. The Champion Fibre Company's timber resources on the Pigeon River headlands lay beyond reach until the railroad was completed, and it looked like the pulp mill would begin operations by the end of the year. The railway company's president, Oma Carr, was also responsible for Champion's wood procurement. Undoubtedly, Mr. Carr did everything in his power to expedite the railroad construction work. Yandle Brothers seemingly reacted to pressure from Carr and others by using more dynamite to blast away the rock and open the deep cuts that the railroad would run through.

On one occasion, as related in Reuben B. Robertson's memoirs, Yandle used so much dynamite that they blasted huge chunks of rock weighing eight to ten tons apiece a distance of one hundred feet beyond the right-of-way. A widow lady who lived in a cabin where a few wayward chunks landed gave the blasting crew a sample of a riled mountain woman's fury. Robertson allowed that from then on all of the chunks blasted were much smaller, giving the impression that Yandle Brothers had learned a lesson and, thereafter, their work became less hurried and not as dangerous.[105]

Still, Yandle Brothers' safety record was anything but safe during that initial year of their contract in 1907. About a month after the grading work began on the Canton-to-Sunburst railroad, an extraordinary accident occurred along the route. It was reported at the time that a premature dynamite explosion near Camp 6 injured eight to ten men, and one was dead.[106] Evidence of still another accident is gleaned from a court settlement, where Mr. Dred Blaylock was awarded five hundred dollars to be paid by Yandle Brothers on account of the death of his son. Ben Blaylock was working in a field when he was fatally injured by Yandle Brothers' blasting operation on the railroad grade located nearby.[107]

For sure, tragedy was no stranger to the Pigeon River Railway construction work. However, another incident that occurred during the last days of summer was beyond anyone's comprehension or belief. Along the railway route, between Camps 5 and 6, a walking boss employed by Yandle's subcontractor was shot and killed by one of the workmen. The boss's name was Gin Grisch, or Blackie as he was commonly known.[108] Blackie had reportedly argued with the killer, George Shelton, the night before. Shelton was walking up the line the following day when he encountered Blackie in his buggy. The boss upbraided Shelton for not being at work, after which Shelton pulled out a revolver and shot Blackie four or five times in rapid succession. Witnesses who heard the shots said they saw Blackie stand up in the buggy and then lunge forward to the ground. Afterward, Shelton fled the scene and the construction site, and despite a regional manhunt, this member of a long-established mountain clan was never apprehended.[109]

Such gruesome details serve to convey a sense of the physical dangers involved in constructing Thomson's grand enterprise and the resulting numerous deaths and injuries that occurred. Besides these awful accidents, the labor strike, and tax troubles, there was still another significant event that brought Thomson's pulp mill project and the railroad construction to a standstill in the fall of 1907. It was called the "Banker's Panic," which took place over a several-week period beginning in mid-October with the collapse of the New York Stock Exchange. There were numerous runs on banks and trust companies as the panic spread across the nation, causing many banks and businesses to declare bankruptcy. Unfortunately, Peter Thomson, the savvy and forethoughtful businessman, was caught off guard, like so many others, and found himself in an over-extended financial condition when the panic struck.

George Smathers said later, "I don't think that I ever met anybody that appeared to be more depressed and bluer than Mr. Thomson appeared to be over the financial situation."[110] Nevertheless, Thomson was not without wealthy friends who apparently were unaffected by the financial turmoil. These included William Cooper Procter, the dynamic head of the Procter and Gamble Company, and Jacob Schmidlapp, one of Cincinnati's most prominent bankers and financiers. Both admired Peter Thomson for his business acumen and steadfast honesty. When they heard of his distressed situation, immediate offers of financial assistance were extended, and Thomson readily availed himself of their aid.

Reuben Robertson wrote that Mr. Procter said to his father-in-law, "Peter, I understand you are in urgent need of funds to carry you through the present emergency, and I want to help. Here is the key to my security box. Go take what you need and let me know the amount." Whether or not you believe this heart-warming claim, one thing is for certain—Thomson took bank loans from his two wealthy benefactors, who in turn accepted shares of Champion Fibre Company's preferred stock as repayment.

The immediate effect of Procter's and Schmidlapp's bailout did not reach Canton in time to prevent a large layoff of the workforce. On November 7th, 1907, about half the workers at the pulp mill were discharged because

of the money stringencies. It was also about this time that the Yandle Brothers' construction work on the Pigeon River Railway was shut down, as another austerity measure.[111] One gripping report indicates that some three hundred to four hundred men were discharged and issued checks, and that some inconvenience was experienced in having these checks cashed at the Champion Bank.

The urgency of the situation at the time can be perceived from the very words of this same *Charlotte Observer* report:

The stringency of the money market is being felt here in the fact that the Champion Fibre Company paid off this week by check instead of in actual cash, as had been their custom. Mr. O.M. Hampton, cashier of the Champion Bank, stated that he had made every effort to secure the money but had been unsuccessful. It is feared that some trouble may result from this as the bank will be able to cash checks very slowly at best, and many of the lower class of laborers regard this as a scheme on the part of the company to keep them out of their money. The merchants and businessmen of the town are doing all they can and it is hoped that any show of disturbance will be avoided.[112]

Fortunately, no violent riots erupted as a result of the layoffs and money troubles evoked by the Banker's Panic. There can be no doubts, however, that much pain was suffered by the construction workers who lost their jobs, as well as the town's citizens. At last, on November 21st, Peter Thomson steamed down to the construction site at Canton and settled the matter once and for all—and rather quickly. After looking over the works and the field, he ordered that all of the laid-off employees should be put back to work, and kept there until the "building of the company is completed," possibly by the last of January, 1908.[113]

Very telling it is that Mr. Thomson had to hurry down to Canton during the midst of the Banker's Panic, assess the construction status at his pulp mill and the workforce situation, and then issue orders to hire all the men back who had been laid off—and keep them on the job until it was done. After all, he had a host of supervisors in Canton to run things—Oma Carr heading up the extract plant and holding the wood procurement responsibilities, Thomas Marr assisting Carr in the extract plant, Jim Harris over the pulp mill and aided by Carl Jentz and Joe Clark, and Charles Bryant in charge of financial and administrative affairs. Additionally, a new member of this Champion Fibre management team had only recently arrived from Ohio to "coordinate" matters, as Reuben B. Robertson later explained his role.

Peter Thomson had been under tremendous strain due to the financial pressures at Hamilton and Canton, which were brought to a head by the Banker's Panic. George Smathers attested to this and a doctor's decision confirmed it when Mr. Thomson was ordered to bed. At the behest of the Thomson family, Reuben B. Robertson went down to Canton—either just before or during the Banker's Panic—to personally coordinate matters at the Champion Fibre Company, which were then in complete disarray. Primarily, he was sent to bring order and resolve the inexplicable jealous disputes, petty discords, and general dysfunction that existed amongst the Champion Fibre bosses. Certainly, it was no small task for the inexperienced Robertson, but it was one in which he had his father-in-law's full backing. To ensure there were no questions at Canton regarding the authority that Reuben Robertson carried in his new coordinator role, Mr. Thomson penned an emphatic note for the Canton bosses:

Nov 4, 1907

Mr. Reuben B. Robertson is hereby given full authority to take entire charge of details of every kind at the plant of the Champion Fibre Co., to employ and discharge hands, and his decisions are to be absolute in all matters.

Peter Thomson
President

As if his son-in-law was going to sea to destroy the enemies and preserve the profits of the great enterprise, Peter Thomson thought it necessary to draft this amazing "Letter of Marque," as it became known, to authorize Robertson's actions. Its broad and powerful terms left no doubts in the minds of the Champion Fibre Company executives concerning the authority and power that Reuben B. Robertson carried with him to Canton. As Robertson recalled much later, this document gave him the organizational respectability he needed at that time, and he was never directly challenged thereafter.[114]

Nevertheless, Robertson either did not have enough time to adjust in his new leadership role or did not possess the means to effect a satisfactory resolution to the Banker's Panic crisis at Canton. He was in charge of the company affairs at the time of the lay-offs, and must have signed off on the actions to "discharge hands." Instead, it was left for Peter Thomson to defy a doctor's orders, summon the physical strength and energies to travel by train from Cincinnati to Canton, and give instructions to hire the workers back and complete his pulp mill.

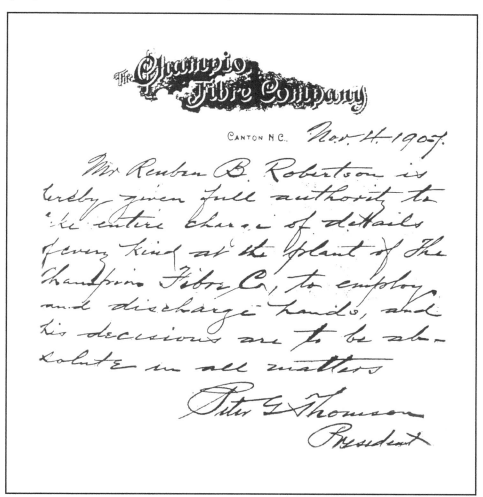

Although the quality of this image is extremely poor, it is a copy of the actual "Letter of Marque" penned by Peter G. Thomson in November, 1907 and sent to the Champion Fibre Company bosses at Canton. In it, Thomson grants unconditional authority to Reuben B. Robertson to coordinate affairs at the plant of the Champion Fibre Company. He also states that Robertson's "decisions are to be absolute." (from Canton Area Historical Museum)

Photos from 1907

In early 1907 the tall soda digester building's roof remains unfinished, as can be seen in this photo. The tannin extract plant's evaporator building is hidden behind scaffolding in the center foreground. Notice the three huge vessels staged on rail cars.

This view to the south in very early 1907 shows the following buildings already under roof: (from right to left) pulp bleaching and pulp beaters, machine room, and pulp storage warehouse. Note the railroad trestle track alongside the pulp storage building to the left. There will be one on the opposite side of the warehouse as well to facilitate loading and shipment of pulp to the Champion Coated Paper Company in Hamilton, Ohio. (from Manufacturer's Record, Jan. 9, 1908)

It is likely that these are three of the four copper evaporators that will be installed inside the evaporator building. Each vessel will be skidded through the large opening left in the north wall, and it is possible that one has already been moved inside. (from Sellars Collection)

The construction site looks desolate in this early 1907 photo, with the sulphite digester house standing prominently in the center. Scaffolding still surrounds the soda digester building behind it. Note the pulp mill machine room and pulp storage warehouse at the right appear to be completed, for the most part. The tall stacks rising from the contractor's sawmill can be seen to the left of the digester buildings. (from Sellars Collection)

An early 1907 wintry view to the south shows many buildings under construction, with the exception of the pulp mill machine room and pulp storage warehouse to the left. Their exteriors look to be mostly finished. The high sulphite digester house has been topped off, and the roof of the soda digester house in front of it is still being erected. In the far distance beyond the digester buildings is the Fincher house, which was built in about 1900. This old house still stands today on Penland Avenue near the Canton Middle School. (from Sellars Collection)

This early 1907 photo shows the soda digester house still shrouded in scaffolding. The brick work is not complete and the roof structure is being erected. In the right foreground, the structural steel roof that can be seen will eventually shelter the causticizing process. (from Sellars Collection)

A view looking southwest in early 1907 shows the completed sulphite digester house on the left, and the soda digester building being fitted with a roof and monitor. The lineup of buildings in the foreground is the tannin extract plant. It appears that the exterior of the evaporator building (extreme left side) is almost complete, with the exception of the windows and the large hole in the wall. Two of four evaporators are staged outside and will eventually be slid through this opening. (from Manufacturer's Record, Jan. 9, 1908)

These are the new company houses in the village of Fibreville, as they appeared during construction in 1907. Note that the same architectural template is being used over and over again (from Canton Area Historical Museum)

A view looking to the northwest in early 1907 shows the enormous soda digester house. Scaffolding completely surrounds the building and a scaffold tower rises up the east wall. It appears that the roof framing work is well underway. Interestingly, the sulphite digester house (out of sight) is casting a shadow upon the concrete wall of the screening and filter rooms in the right foreground. (from Sellars Collection)

This view in the spring of 1907 is to the southeast, and shows the extract plant's boiler house building finally under construction. The brick walls that are visible appear to be complete, but the windows have not been installed. Note that the tall soda digester house (the one to the left) appears to be finished, at last. (from Sellars Collection)

Another photo taken in the spring of 1907 offers a view to the east across piles of scrap construction materials. Both towering digester houses are finally topped out, and their scaffolding works have been removed. Construction activities have begun on the wood preparation buildings at the far right and the extract plant boiler house on the left side. To the extreme left a pile driver is at work where a railroad trestle is planned. The reclaiming building in the center appears to be close to completion. (from Sellars Collection)

In this spring or early summer 1907 view of the mill looking to the south, both boiler houses can be seen under construction. The extract plant boiler house is on the far right. To the left of the soda digester building (the closer of the two tall buildings) is the main boiler house with its steel roof structure clearly in place.

Construction of the main smokestack has not started yet. On the right side of this image and next to the river, a plume of smoke rises above Gilbreth Company's steam-driven concrete manufacturing plant. (from Sellars Collection)

This mid-1907 view is to the southeast toward the reclaiming building on the left and wood preparation buildings to the right. Smoke likely spewed from morning until dark out of the tall stacks above the contractor's sawmill. (from Sellars Collection)

Shown here is the Heine boiler installation in progress at the main boiler house. Note the large rounded hole that was broken out of the brick wall so that these boilers could be moved inside the building. There will eventually be twenty boilers (ten on each side of the boiler room) installed over brick furnaces. (from Sellars Collection)

Standing N. W. Looking N. E. over Champion Fiber Mills, Canton, N. C.

The building marked (1) is the one in which our boilers are and is as it looks today. Building (2) is the Heiney boiler house.

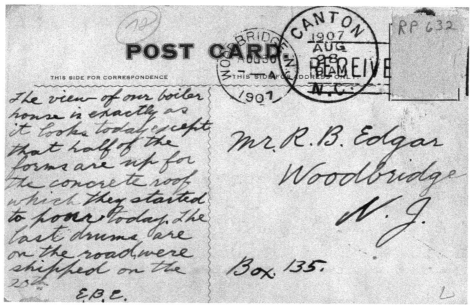

These two images represent the front and back side of a postcard mailed to Woodbridge, New Jersey in late August, 1907. The card proved to be very enlightening and helpful in identifying the likely manufacturer of the extract plant's boilers. "EBE," or Ellis B. Edgar, writes from Canton to his brother Ralph B. Edgar, pointing out in the postcard photo where "our" boilers are located. Apparently, Ellis was a representative of a boiler company and further research tied these two brothers to Ellis F. Edgar, who was not only their father but a prolific inventor of boiler machinery living in Woodbridge as well. The extract plant boilers are thought to have been supplied and installed by the Edgar Boiler Company of New York City, the manufacturer of Ellis F. Edgar's boilers and furnaces. (from Canton Area Historical Museum)

Inside the extract plant boiler house, boiler drums (steam drum on top and mud drum at bottom) and tubing can be seen hanging from structural steel supports in the background. In the foreground, work is underway connecting tubing to another steam drum. The extract plant's boilers are believed to have been furnished by the Edgar Boiler Company of New York City, as evidenced by the square-headed rivets installed in the steam drum. These rivets would eventually support a firebrick arch at the top of the furnace, as patented by Ellis F. Edgar in 1903. (from Sellars Collection)

Although difficult to see in this photo, work is in progress installing an induced draft fan in the extract plant boiler house. The fan is designed to pull the smoke and air from the boiler furnaces and discharge it into a large stack piercing the roof. (from Sellars Collection)

Barely discernible in this photo is a brave man working high up on the smokestack above the extract plant boiler house. (from Sellars Collection)

The 520-feet long conveyor house can be seen under construction in this photo. It will house a conveyor to transport spruce and hemlock refuse from the wood preparation buildings to the tannin extract plant on the right. (from Sellars Collection)

These carpenters are taking a much-needed break in their job of building a 520-feet long conveyor house. When completed, a Link-Belt conveyor will be installed inside, stretching between the wood preparation buildings and the tannin extract plant (shown here). It will be used to transport spruce and hemlock refuse to the extract plant. (from Sellars Collection)

This busy photo shows ironworkers erecting structural steel building framing. A timber gin pole located in the center of the building is being employed to hoist the heavy steel beams and move them into place. This was extremely dangerous work, and several unfortunate accidents did occur at the Champion Fibre Company site. (from Sellars Collection)

Shown here is one of the reported "thousand" railcar loads of equipment received at the mill during construction. (from Sellars Collection)

This photo taken in the fall of 1907 is a north-facing view of the extract plant boiler house. A man can barely be seen working at the smokestack. Piles protruding out of the ground in the forefront will likely support a long refuse conveyor house, yet to be started. (from Sellars Collection)

Inclined ladders accessing the inside of these enormous vessels suggest there is work to be done in there—perhaps the construction of firebrick linings. These are the rotary furnaces used in the soda recovery process. (from Sellars Collection)

Ironworkers pose precariously on top of the structural steel framework for the main boiler house's roof and coal bin. There is no evidence of safety harnesses and ropes, or any other measures to protect these men from falls. Behind them, the sulphite digester house looks to be in good order, and the digesters and associated piping and equipment are surely being installed inside. (from Sellars Collection)

A view to the southeast in mid-1907 shows the reclaiming room with a large smoke stack above the furnaces protruding through the roof. The building in the lower-left corner is the evaporator room. Dark smoke billows out of one of the busy sawmill's stacks. (from Sellars Collection)

Workmen are putting the finishing touches on the main smokestack in this late summer 1907 view. The concrete chimney towers over the 100-feet high soda digester house, with the following three smaller buildings in the foreground: (from left to right) the evaporator building, causticizing room, and reclaiming room. (from Sellars Collection)

A midsummer 1907 photo looking to the west shows the main concrete smokestack nearly topped out. The color of the concrete chimney appears darker the higher up one looks, a good indication of the curing process.

Scaffolding surrounds the generator room to the right of the huge chimney. Gilbreth Company's construction office is to the left of the smokestack and in front of the tall sulphite digester building on the left. (from Sellars Collection)

After the main smokestack was completed in the summer of 1907, an intrepid photographer was willing to climb up the scaffolding on the inside of the chimney to capture these two views. The photo above is a shot to the north over the tannin extract plant. In the one below, he aimed his camera to the west over the soda digester house. The extract plant's buildings are on the right side, where the refuse boiler house can be seen under construction. (from Sellars Collection)

This photo shows a room full of steel tanks and tank bottoms. These vessels were likely being built in the causticizing building, which contained twenty-six tanks that were each 15-1/2 feet in diameter. (from Sellars Collection)

Since the leaves have not yet fallen from the trees, this wonderful eastward-looking photo was probably taken in the fall of 1907. The main boiler house and smokestack appear to be complete, situated between the finished digester houses. To the left, the extract plant boiler house is still behind scaffolding and apparently not complete.

Also, construction of the 520-feet long housed conveyor stretching between the wood preparation buildings and the tannin extract plant has just been started. Note that pulp wood is already being received and stored in long piles on the river side of the mill. (from Sellars Collection)

Several of the buildings associated with Thomson's pulp mill had walls and floors made of reinforced concrete to better resist chemical and humid environments. This is a photo of one such building. Timber columns and roof beams were also used in this instance. (from Sellars Collection)

An eastward view shows the Southern Railroad's deep cut with the main rail line running through it. The Southern's depot can be seen just behind a train of parked railcars in the right foreground. Vital sidetracks branch off the main line and run onto the eastern mill grounds. The dirt road climbing the hillside on the left follows the path of today's Newfound Street.

A view to the northeast shows a dirt road running around the hillside that is generally located along the path of today's Champion Drive. To the left are several small company houses (similar to the ones constructed at Fibreville) situated on the hill north of the pulp mill and extract plant. On the right side of the photo can be seen the Campground Branch drainage gulley covered in thick vegetation and a few outbuildings. A burgeoning community of comfortable frame homes sprawls over the hillsides located in the vicinity of today's North Main Street.

This scene offers an early view of Canton to the southeast. The vertical pole in the center of the image is a lightning rod installed on top of Champion's 250-feet high concrete chimney. Across the bottom of the photo, buildings line Canton's Main Street. A singular dwelling with a hint of a pyramidal roof appears in this lineup, located just to the left of the lightning rod. It will very soon be modified and converted into a hotel. The structure still stands today and continues to serve the citizens of Canton as a popular restaurant. (These three photographs—bottom of opposite page and above—are from a series of at least four photos taken from atop the Champion Fibre Company's new smokestack—Sellars' collection).

In this amazing photo taken during the fall of 1907 most of the building exteriors appear to be complete, with the exception of the extract plant boiler house at the far left. Construction sheds, building materials, and living quarters are still highly visible, as are the sawmill's tall smokestacks. The Dr. Moore house remains standing in the center foreground and the cribbed retaining wall can be seen running along the river.

Through the Southern Railway bridge's iron trusses, the river pump house can barely be detected. On the hillside beyond the tall sulphite digester building and smokestack, seven company houses have been constructed to supplement those in Fibreville. (from Sellars Collection)

In the summer of 1907, the huge 250-feet high smokestack associated with the main boiler house was constructed. As can be seen, the men worked from scaffolding built inside the circular stack, forming and pouring concrete in five-foot sections every day. Their method was to install the iron reinforcing bars, winch the metal molds up five feet at a time, and then cast the concrete before daylight gave out. If one looks close enough, the dimension 17'-0" can be seen on the outside of the mold, indicating the outside diameter of the smokestack. (from Sellars Collection)

Chapter 8
1908—Startup

During the latter part of 1907, farmers living and working around Canton and preparing for another cold winter spotted it from miles away. Seemingly towering into the clouds, Champion Fibre Company's new smokestack had finally begun to spew smoke from its flared top, two hundred and fifty feet above the ground. The pulp mill's two mammoth digester buildings were dwarfed by this monolith that had stood idle for months while its eighteen-inch thick walls of reinforced concrete cured and became harder every day.

One of Gilbreth's pile-driving teams had sunk two hundred timber piles to support the structure, which was constructed by Alphons Custodis Chimney Construction Company of New York City.[115] This company, which specialized in large chimney projects, created the circular shape by pouring concrete into metal molds. Every day they cast a seventeen-foot diameter by five-foot high section, working from scaffolding built inside the smokestack's round wall. The workmen's method was to place the reinforcing iron bars, winch the molds up five feet at a time, and pour the concrete before each day's end. This procedure was repeated every day until the chimney crew had completed its daunting task in less than two month's time.

The dark smoke escaping from the top of the smokestack could mean only one thing: Peter Thomson's great enterprise was in the throes of start-up. Hundreds of brand new machines had to be tested, and the first attempts were being made to produce steam and electricity to run them. Start-up was an inherently difficult and complicated process that required troubleshooting, tuning, and making modifications to each piece of equipment in the mill before operations could successfully begin. Of course, the dark spewing smoke above the plant indicated that the boiler fires were lit, which was the start of start-up.

The Champion Fibre Company's main boiler house was the most modern in the country at the time, housing twenty water-tube boilers. These were manufactured by the Heine Safety Boiler Company and each one had a capacity to produce 316 horsepower of energy. Raging fires within the enormous coal-burning furnaces were automatically fed by chutes running from overhead coal bins. These combustions rendered not only heat, but hot ash and cinders that were automatically discharged and conveyed into railcars for disposal. The column of smoke escaping from the giant smokestack was created by the Heine boilers being put to the test for the first time.

Steam produced from the boilers was used to generate electricity, run the variable speed machinery, and provide heat to the numerous processes that required it. One-hundred-and-fifty-pound steam was piped to the generator room next door and fed

into two enormous Hamilton-Corliss cross-compound steam engines. These powerful engines—1,800 horsepower each—drove two 1,500 kilowatt generators, which produced three-phase, 440-volt, alternating electrical current. Approximately 120 miles of wiring snaked throughout the plant, connecting motors and lighting fixtures to the electrical source at the generator room's switching center.[116] Electric motors, relatively novel devices at the time, were used all through the plant to power the bulk of the process machinery, with the exception of the steam-driven variable-speed machines.

Only after the boilers, water and steam piping, automatic fire protection, and electrical systems were trouble free and operational, did the start-up of the many distinct mill processes go ahead.[117] By most accounts, the sulphite-pulping process was the first to begin trial operations, and by January 18, 1908, or thereabouts, the first stiff gray pulp was produced. An Asheville newspaper reported that "the great Champion Fibre company of Canton has begun operations. Not all the plant is complete, but part of it is ready for operation, and on Saturday the first run was made, and the machinery worked with perfect success."[118]

Actually, only the sulphite-pulping process had started up with "perfect success." This was the one that used spruce wood, and sometimes hemlock and balsam when there was a shortage of spruce, to make into a high-grade "long-fiber" pulp. Spruce could not be obtained from Sunburst at that early date because the Pigeon River

Railway's road from Canton to Sunburst had not been completed. In fact, Yandle Brothers was shut down in November, 1907 as a result of the Banker's Panic, and progress on the railroad was lagging woefully behind schedule. As it turned out, Yandle did not go back to work until the latter part of 1908, and the railroad was not completed until five years later. However, Champion Fibre Company had found other sources of spruce and chestnut to supply the pulp mill and tannin extract plant.[119]

During most of 1907, Champion was stocking vast piles of spruce and chestnut pulpwood on the company's property wherever there was available space. The wood was purchased from local loggers and various independent timber operations throughout western North Carolina. But after the sulphite mill operations started up, it became more and more difficult to obtain sufficient quantities of spruce, hemlock, and balsam from these small and unreliable sources. So to "keep at least two jumps ahead of the sheriff," as Reuben Robertson later explained, Champion Fibre Company acquired another small tract of land located on the crest of the nearby Plott Balsam Mountains in Jackson County.

This tract was covered with a dense stand of spruce, which Champion quickly endeavored to get out. The big spruce logs were snaked out of the forest by the usual methods of horse, mule, and oxen teams and hauled to a cut-up mill. Here they were sawn into 30-inch billets and then split into flume-size pieces. The split wood fell directly from the splitter into a flume (similar to the one Montgomery Smith had proposed to connect Sunburst with Canton) and was then sluiced for a distance of five miles, directly into waiting rail cars at the town of Addie. Long train loads of spruce were pulled the relatively short distance from Addie to Canton along the tracks of the Murphy Branch of the Southern Railway.[120]

Reuben Robertson and Oma Carr considered this as only an interim solution to the spruce-sourcing problem. With the Pigeon River headlands beyond the reach of reliable transportation for the time being, the Champion bosses desperately worked to develop other means to supply the pulp mill and extract plant with wood. As one strategy, they purchased the Quinlan-Monroe Lumber Company in Haywood County, which held extensive stands of spruce along the headwaters of Richland Creek. Development of this property required substantial infrastructure work to get the wood out of the forest. A Roebling incline rail system powered by a stationary steam engine was installed to lower the timber off the high slopes. Additionally, the existing wooden-railed, gravity tram road running from the woods operation to the Southern line near Waynesville was refurbished with iron rails. This project was undertaken in order to accommodate a new Heisler steam locomotive which replaced the teams hauling tram cars back to the woods. By mid-1908, loaded tram cars were finally rolling out of the mountains over new iron rails to nearby

Hazelwood, where the Southern's tracks were less than ten miles from Canton.[121] For the time being, then, the Quinlan-Monroe timber operation allowed Robertson and Oma Carr to focus on other important things, such as the production problems incurred with Carr's "double-use" pulping technology.

Startup of the soda-pulping process proved much more problematic than the sulphite pulp mill. The soda mill was intrinsically linked to the design of the tannin extract plant, and the plan was to use chestnut wood along with Oma Carr's patented wood chipper and double-use methodology. Peter Thomson had been sold on Carr's ideas from the start. However, until early 1908 when everything was finally ready to be placed into operation, Carr's ideas had been based on experiments and pilot-plant tests only.

His new chipper was radically different from those commonly used in pulp mills, in that it cut chestnut chips in the direction of the wood's grain into thin shavings. The normal chippers took the sticks of wood end on, cutting against the grain and producing bulkier wood chips with shorter fiber lengths. Carr's experiments had proven that the thin chip shavings could be preserved in the tannin acid extraction process and still be used afterward to produce soda pulp. This was his double-use technology that had been patented but not tested in a full-scale mill operation.

Hopes were high and nerves twitching during the initial start-up runs of the extract plant and soda mill in early 1908. But there were problems. The double-use chestnut chips sent from the extract department to the soda digesters were "fluffy," as Reuben B. Robertson remembered, and did not pack inside the digesters to give a full yield. It was like "packing feathers" is how he likened the peculiar conditions. As a result, the mill production capability was lowered substantially. Another drawback with re-using the chestnut chips was the high moisture content carried over from the extract plant—almost double that of the poplar chips in a conventional soda-pulping process. These significant problems, or variances, not only created production shortfalls, but they threw out of kilter the standard liquor and chemical recovery balances.

It took Champion Fibre's employees several years of heart-breaking struggles and adjustments to resolve these pulping problems. In the meantime, poplar wood was substituted to make a "short-fiber" pulp using the traditional soda-pulping process, while chestnut was chipped and ground for the extraction process. Eventually, after going back to chipping the chestnut wood billets end on, but with modifications, and making adaptations for the excessive moisture conditions, the double-use problems were overcome. The success that Oma Carr had promised was actually realized, and for many years to come Champion enjoyed "costless" pulp in the soda mill. Reuben B. Robertson later wrote, "the double-use process proved to be one of the most profitable of all Champion activities and amply justified the patient waiting that was involved."[122, 123]

Much finishing, painting, and cleanup work was left to do during the first half of 1908. Undoubtedly, there were other pieces of equipment besides Carr's chipper that did not perform as expected, and these required modifications or replacement. Photos taken late in the construction period indicate that the long, housed conveyor designed to extend from the wood preparation buildings on the south side of the mill to the extract plant on the north side is not yet in place. Also missing is the conveyor from the wood prep area to the sulphite digester building. It was fundamental that these and other conveyors be finished prior to startup. So their installations were likely rushed to completion and "field-engineered." That is, they were built on-site to fit with minimal engineering.

Come June, 1908, the Champion Fibre Company was shipping eight to ten rail car loads of pulp daily to Peter Thomson's coated paper mill in Hamilton, Ohio. Additionally, several car loads of tannic acid were going out every week. Pulpwood was being consumed at a rate of eight to ten railcar loads per day and the Heine boilers were burning about one hundred and forty tons of coal every single day.[124] Champion Fibre Company's seven hundred employees were keeping the Southern Railway's tracks busy and the lumber men's axes and saws cutting—but not cutting fast enough it seems. The supplies of pulpwood purchased from independent timber operators and those obtained from scattered company-owned tracts barely sufficed to keep Champion Fibre "ahead of the sheriff."

Inadequate funds continued to hinder progress on the Pigeon River Railway to Sunburst, and the valuable timber located on the Pigeon River headlands remained inaccessible. Consequently, Thomson and Robertson availed themselves of a business opportunity that would allow them to contract for a twenty-year supply of pulpwood for the Canton Mill. In early 1911, they allied Champion Fibre Company with the interests of William Whitmer & Sons. This northern investment concern controlled the new Champion Lumber Company that owned several vast boundaries of virgin timber in western North Carolina. Hard as it must have been for them, Thomson and Robertson decided to exchange their ownership of the unfinished Pigeon River Railway and the timberlands surrounding Sunburst for the guarantee of a pulpwood supply from Champion Lumber.

By 1912, Champion Fibre Company had agreed to purchase from Champion Lumber a minimum of one hundred cords of spruce and hemlock per working day at fixed prices set by contract. Thomson and Robertson also committed to buy at market price all of the chestnut cordwood that Champion Lumber could cut, up to one hundred cords per day.[125, 126] Although this contract relieved Peter Thomson of his treasured Pigeon River headlands and the railroad to Sunburst, it also relieved Reuben B. Robertson of the pulpwood supply problems at his father-in-law's mill. With this agreement in place, Robertson could direct his full energies toward the operation of the

Champion Fibre Company. It was absolutely imperative that the maximum tonnage of pulp and tannin extract—and more—be produced. After all, the Hamilton mill had to be supplied, debts had to be repaid, enormous operating expenses met, and stockholders' interests honored. Not to mention, there was also the "sheriff" who must be kept at bay.

Peter Thomson's surrogate and son-in-law, Reuben B. Robertson, ran and administered things in Canton from the days of startup, as the mill began to grow steadily. A sulphate pulp mill was added in 1919 to give the mill an additional ability to convert more species of coniferous trees (pine trees) into bleached pulp. In the early 1920's, an electrolytic bleach plant and two paper machines were installed at Canton. This was the advent of fine paper production at the Champion Fibre Company plant, with the new paper-making facility producing one hundred tons of book and bond paper each day.

Mr. Robertson's attentions and extraordinary efforts during those early years following the founding of the Champion Fibre Company were not wholly devoted to increasing production and profits at the Canton facility. With Peter Thomson's blessings, of course, he was able to address other pressing infrastructure needs. A decade after start-up of the Champion Fibre Company, a new main office building was constructed that was both commodious and conspicuously handsome, manifesting a modern professional look of which the

mill bosses, employees, and citizens were justifiably proud. It would at last replace the nineteenth-century Nelse Mease house that had served as the general office building for Champion Fibre Company from the early days of the plant's construction.[127]

In 1920, construction of an even larger and more magnificent brick edifice was completed to house the new Champion YMCA. This structure, erected at a cost of $75,000 adjacent to the new main office, was intended to benefit not only young men and company employees, but the entire community as well. The multiple-story building had an expansive covered porch supported by a row of paired Doric columns that welcomed members and visitors. In very little time the "Champion Y" became the town center of physical fitness as well as cultural and civic activities of every description.

There was also Champion's commissary business that Peter G. Thomson held over the heads of Canton's Big Five during the mill's construction period. Apparently, the early tax troubles were so irksome that Thomson was motivated to establish a company commissary soon after start-up. For years the store operated in whatever space could be spared in the mill. But by the mid-1920's, a company store for employees was operating out of a new brick building adjacent to the recently opened YMCA. It was a clean and friendly place where employees and their families could purchase food and all types of general merchandise at bargain prices. Why, it was even possible for mill employees to use company scrip—called "doogaloo" by the mill employees—to trade for items in Champion Fibre's company store.[128]

Although production was always the key factor in Champion's success formula, Reuben B. Robertson never allowed his superintendents to lose sight of the employees' safety and welfare. The company housing, employee store, and new Champion YMCA were brick and mortar evidence of the paternalistic culture that Robertson fostered throughout the years. And, yes, the fact that the company printed its own money—or doogaloo—could be interpreted as still another effort to ease the lives of Champion's employees.

———

Unquestionably, the founding of the pulp mill in Canton was due to the initiatives, energies, and sacrifices of Peter G. Thomson, a veritable force-of-nature. President Thomson led his new western North Carolina enterprise to the highest summits of success and profitability. Although the initial plan was for Reuben B. Robertson to return to Hamilton, Ohio after the Champion Fibre Company mill was up and running, he never did. Instead, Mr. Robertson held on to that "Letter of Marque" his father-in-law had penned, and guided the development of the Canton mill as it became the largest pulp and paper manufacturing facility in the world.

He was the boots-on-the-ground leader of the Champion Fibre Company, while bugs were gradually worked out of the chemical pulping processes, machinery was

optimized, facilities expanded, and pulpwood resources secured. For many years, Reuben Robertson served as General Manager of the Champion Fibre Company and its forest-lands. In 1935, when the Canton and Hamilton mills were joined with a new plant in Houston, Texas to form the huge Champion Paper and Fibre Company, Mr. Robertson was elected vice president. Eleven years later the presidency became his and, finally, he was elected chairman of the board of directors in 1950.

Robertson often quipped that he "came down to Canton for a fifty-day assignment, which turned out to be a fifty-year assignment!"[129]

No one benefitted more from that prolonged mission than the Champion employees and citizens of Canton, who were the beneficiaries of this personable man's dedication and leadership. Generations of Canton men, women, and their families were able to enjoy increased prosperity and cultural opportunities derived from the success of the town's pulp and paper mill.

Champion's original giant smokestack is currently being demolished (2018) and the Heine boilers are long since gone. New and more efficient gas-fueled steam-production systems power the paper and board manufacturing facility that exists today. However, concealed within those tons of structural steel and siding there still remain very old foundations, brick walls, and timber structures from Peter Thomson's original pulp mill. No doubt, there is life and purpose in them yet.

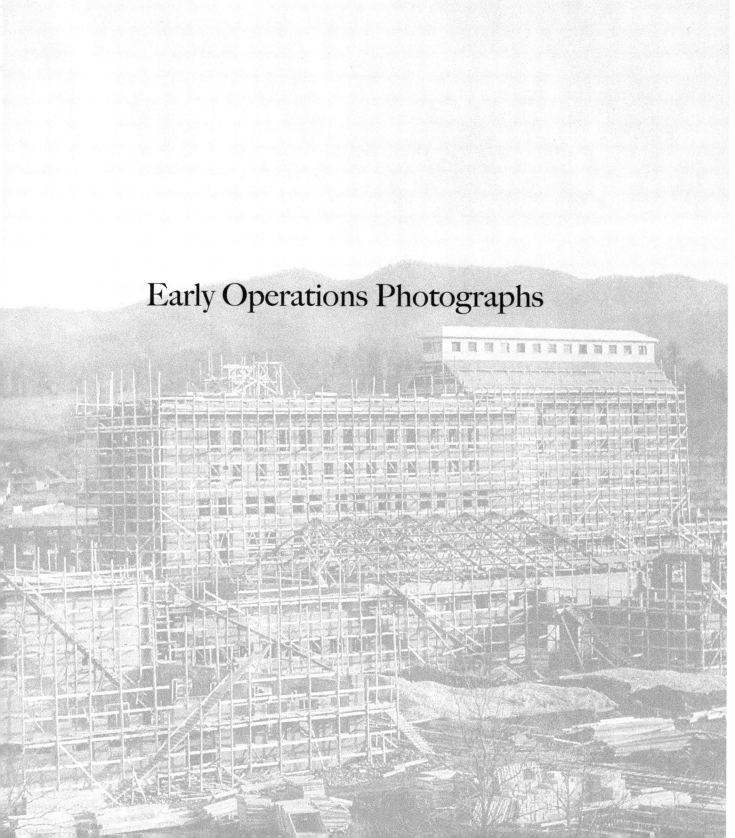

Early Operations Photographs

PLANT OF CHAMPION FIBRE CO., CANTON, NORTH CAROLINA.

The penny postcard rendering shown above depicts the mill in operation soon after the 1908 startup. For some reason the red-brick generator room in the center appears to be white (probably to highlight it). Pulp wood stored in towering stacks dwarfs the puffing steam engine at work in the woodyard. (from Canton Area Historical Museum)

Presented below is the actual photographic image used to craft the penny postcard. It is a view to the west and the "white" generator building pictured on the postcard now shows its true colors. (from Sellars Collection)

A view to the north shows the mill in full operation. The "sea of bottomless mud" has been replaced with brick buildings and a sea of pulp wood. Note the steam engine at work in the woodyard. (from Canton Area Historical Museum)

There would certainly have been a change in the air in Canton with the startup of the Champion Fibre Company plant in 1908. This photo taken in the very early years of operation shows that the mill is already undergoing an expansion. A new building is being constructed at the west end of the extract plant boiler house (left foreground). As can easily be seen, every available square foot of space is filled with pulp wood. (from Canton Area Historical Museum)

In 1910, two years after startup, solutions to the mill's pulp wood handling and storage problems on the south side appear to be evolving, as can be seen in the panoramic photo above. The shortage of space eventually led to the purchase of the Penland property, directly across the river. (from Canton Area Historical Museum)

The panoramic view of Canton and the Champion Fibre Company shown below was captured in about 1910. The photographer set up on a hill to the south of the mill and aimed the camera northward to capture the image. Smoke is spewing from every stack and pulp wood is abundant. Railcars are stretched out on the Southern Railway's line running across the center of the photo. On the extreme right, note the location of the highway crossing over the Pigeon River. At that place, upstream of the railroad bridge, an iron-truss bridge fabricated in Canton, Ohio spans the river. This bridge provided the inspiration for town fathers to adopt the name "Canton." It was installed circa 1892 and demolished in 1962. (from Canton Area Historical Museum)

Peter Gibson Thomson, Sr. (from Canton Area Historical Museum)

Biographical Profile of
Peter G. Thomson, Sr.

Peter Gibson Thomson was referred to as a "force of nature" in the closing paragraphs of the previous chapter. This analogy should not be construed as an exaggeration. On the contrary, it is considered an apt appraisal of the man who demonstrated such unlimited perseverance and energies, tenacity of purpose, and resourcefulness in founding his pulp mill enterprise in Canton, North Carolina. Details provided in this book of the tremendous undertaking to build the Champion Fibre Company pulp mill provide ample evidence that Peter Thomson was a man to be reckoned with. However, this story has not delved into his early formative years and the making of the businessman who founded the Champion Coated Paper Company in Hamilton, Ohio. For that reason an abbreviated profile of Peter Thomson's life and career leading up to his explorations in western North Carolina is given herein.

The young businessman Peter G. Thomson is stand-ing second from the right and wearing a derby hat in this 1877 photo. Twenty-five years old at the time, he is posing with colleagues in front of his bookstore at 179 Vine Street in Cincinnati, Ohio. (UNCA Ramsey Library Special Collections)

Some said that Peter Gibson Thomson inherited his virtues of honesty and hard work from his parents—a Scots father and Welsh mother. Unfortunately, his father, Alexander Thomson, died in 1864 of rheu-matic fever. Peter was only twelve years old. A devoted mother, Mary Ann, was left alone to raise Peter and his two sisters, Mollie and Rhoda. Mary Ann's encouragement and sup-port enabled her son to become an honor student at the Second Intermediate School on Ninth Street in Cincinnati. Somehow, she

was later able to scrape together fifty dollars for tuition at the Bryant, Stratton, and DeHan's Commercial Institute in Cincinnati, allowing Peter to continue his studies there.

Perhaps it was his fondness for literature that caused him to go to work as a shipping clerk at the Cincinnati book store, Robert Clarke & Company. Twenty years old when he began, the six formative years that Peter worked for proprietor Robert Clarke—a scholar himself and a generous employer—nurtured his love of books and provided him an invaluable knowledge of printing, paper quality, book binding, and the book market.

These book pursuits and interests did not demand all of Peter's time, though. For years he had been exceedingly conscious of his physical fitness and religiously worked out in a gymnasium. At the age of twenty-two, he was fit enough to set a local gymnasium record for the dead lift and win a prize for Indian club swinging. At about this same time, in the fall of 1874, his attention was aroused in something other than books and physical fitness. Through the Kendrick neigh-bor girls who lived across the street from his home, Peter became acquainted with Miss Laura Gamble. He accepted the Kendricks' invitation to escort Laura to an opera, and subsequently fell hopelessly in love with the Louisville, Kentucky belle before they even reached the theatre house. Amorous senti-ments were mutually shared and, after seeing each other only seven more times, Peter and Laura were married a year later in 1875.

Anxious to find a way to make a comfort-able living for himself and his new bride, Peter took out a loan sometime in 1877 and opened his own book store at 179 Vine Street in Cincinnati. The first few years brought only modest success, until the business was expanded by purchasing another building on Baymiller Street and installing more printing and binding equipment. Peter and Laura's desire to branch out and begin printing and publishing children's books, valentines, and other card and novelty products inspired their business decision. Laura herself became heavily involved in the enterprise by writing verses for the books and cards. Although faced with the supremacy of a strong competitor at the time—McLaughlin and Company in Brooklyn, New York—the Thomsons' printing and publishing business enjoyed modest success, until disaster struck!

One night in October, 1884, a raging fire swept through the structure on Baymiller Street where their printing and publishing business was housed, and almost everything was destroyed. The estimated loss of $75,000 was only partially covered by insurance. Seemingly undaunted, it did not take long for the couple to shake off the bad luck, pick up the pieces, and try again. Peter sold the book store on Vine Street, collected insurance on the Baymiller building fire loss, salvaged some of the damaged equipment, and re-opened their printing and publishing business in a six-story leased building at 258–260 Race Street. By early December, the new factory was open for business and not one Christmas holiday order was lost.

Before long things were back on track and going as well as possible, considering the stiff competition from the much larger New York company, McLaughlin. Eventually, however, Peter could no longer tolerate, nor afford, the price-cutting pressures from McLauglin. So he determined to get out of the business, provided he could do so without incurring a loss. Certainly his business was tiny compared to the huge McLaughlin and Company, but he recognized that it represented a prickly thorn that they would rather be rid of, sooner than later. Knowing that McLaughlin would heighten their efforts to squash his business if they knew he was giving up, Peter devised a negotiation strategy and made a trip to Brooklyn to call at McLaughlin and Company. An interesting account of the subsequent meeting with the McLaughlin interests was published in an 1887 issue of *The Cincinnati Times Star*. It bears repeating here only because it demonstrates Peter's keen senses for business and human nature.

After being ushered directly to a private office and exchanging a few introductory words and niceties with McLaughlin himself, Peter forthrightly announced, "I want to buy this establishment."

"But this establishment is not for sale," he was told.

"But there must be some figure at which you will sell," Peter insisted. "Some figure up in the millions."

"No, there isn't. We are not in the selling out business. We are buying out, we are. We will buy you out."

"But I don't want to sell," said Mr. Thomson.

"You must have some price, up in the

148

thousands," said McLaughlin, paraphrasing Mr. Thomson's remark of a few moments before.

"Yes, I confess I have a price," yielded Mr. Thomson, feigning great reluctance.

"Name it," demanded the head of the firm.

"Not less than one hundred thousand."

"We'll take it," McLaughlin instantly came back, "provided you guarantee never to reengage in this kind of business."

Mr. Thomson agreed.[130]

By this time, the Thomson family had grown significantly. Besides writing verse and stories for books, Laura had been fortunate enough to give birth to five children: Peter Gibson, Jr., Alexander, Mary Belle, Logan, and Hope. Using some of the profit realized from the sale of his printing and publishing business, Peter moved the large family to College Hill, located north of Cincinnati and near Hamilton. From there he began trying to figure out what to do next, while exploring the business opportunities in the area. There were several small paper manufacturers on the Great Miami River running through Hamilton, a manufacturing town hosting a population of about twenty thousand people. It is likely that this Miami River paper industry stoked Peter's still-burning interest to remain in the printing business.

All of Peter's previous book store and printing experience had given him a thorough understanding of the qualities of paper that offered the best base to print on. He was also keen to a new reproduction technology known as half-tone, which was sweeping across the country. With the realization that this technique required a high-quality coated paper, he astutely reckoned there would be a great demand for such a product. It was a notion he could not ignore. After extensive dealings and negotiations with the Champion Card and Paper Company in East Pepperell, Massachusetts, which held the patents on coating machines and a monopoly on manufacturing coated paper, he wrangled a deal that allowed him to open up his own coated paper manufacturing facility in Hamilton. But it came with obligations.

In the fall of 1893, the Champion Coated Paper Company was incorporated as the western branch of Champion Card and Paper Company, with Peter G. Thomson as the president of the company. A total of $100,000 of capital stock was issued, with fifty percent of it going to the East Pepperell company in payment for the perpetual right to use its patents on the coating machines. Thomson declared his territory to cover all of the west and south and that "hereafter orders for enameled book, lithographic, and label papers will be supplied from this mill, while the mill at East Pepperell, Massachusetts will confine its trade in these goods to the eastern market."[131]

A new gas-lit plant was soon constructed on the Great Miami and in April, 1894, one coating machine driven by a single 175-horsepower steam engine went online. By the end of the year, there were four coaters in operation along with calenders and cutters, and the number of employees had increased from ten to twenty-five. The company thrived and the demand for its coated paper grew quickly. Within a year, Peter Thomson had purchased back the stock owned by Champion Card and Paper Company, giving him sole control of the Champion Coated Paper Company. And by early 1896, a new addition to his coating mill was built, increasing the number of machines that coated paper procured from local paper mills to eleven.

At the dawn of the twentieth century, Peter Thomson's thriving company was the largest paper-coating producer in the world, with an output capacity larger than all the other mills in the United States combined. The small paper mills on the Great Miami River in Hamilton became unable to keep up with the Champion Coated Paper Company's demand for paper. So Peter Thomson decided to purchase and install his own paper machines to meet the supply requirements. Mr. Jim Harris was recruited from the Oxford Paper Company to run all aspects of the paper production department. Eventually, he convinced Peter Thomson of the necessity to fully integrate the company by producing its own high-quality pulp to supply the paper machines. Of course, that is where this book started with the search for a pulp mill site in western North Carolina.

Thomson eventually built the Champion Fibre Company in Canton, North Carolina, and by mid-1908 the plant was shipping up to 200 tons daily of sulphite and soda pulp to the Hamilton paper and coating mill. The Canton mill grew steadily over the coming years under the personal and able direction of Mr. Thomson's son-in-law, Reuben

B. Robertson. In fact, it became an industry leader and the largest pulp and paper manufacturer in the world.

Attorney George H. Smathers, a man who had worked long and hard for Peter Thomson to found the Champion Fibre Company in Canton, once told his boss that if he had Thomson's money, he "would take life easy and live on it, and not be bothered with the trouble of building pulp mills and extract plants..." Mr. Thomson's reply bespeaks the unique qualities that filled him. "I believe the man who accumulated wealth had accumulated the same either directly or indirectly by the labor of other people and should use the same for the benefit of mankind." Additionally, he believed "the construction of the pulp mill and extract plant at Canton would prove a great blessing to the people of Haywood County and western North Carolina." His assessment proved to be right of course.

The Ohioan who had expended so much of his energies to build Thomson's pulp mill and who was convinced that his factory would "give employment to people who were out of work and wanted to make an honest living" died on July 10, 1931 at the age of seventy-nine. By then, Reuben B. Robertson, Sr. was steadily guiding the Canton mill, with the prudent advice of Father-in-Law Thomson forever ingrained in his head—"Keep production costs down and sales up."[132, 133, 134, 135]

Reuben Buck Robertson, Sr. (Canton Area Historical Museum)

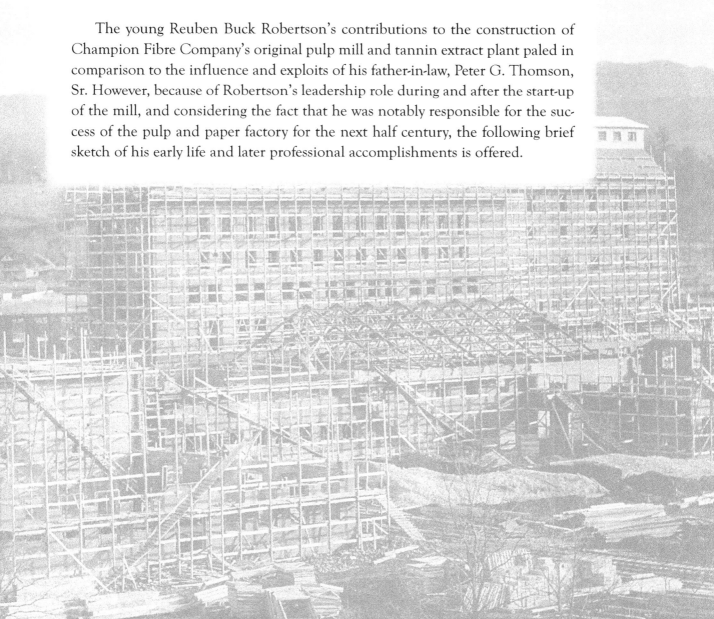

Biographical Profile of
Reuben B. Robertson, Sr.

The young Reuben Buck Robertson's contributions to the construction of Champion Fibre Company's original pulp mill and tannin extract plant paled in comparison to the influence and exploits of his father-in-law, Peter G. Thomson, Sr. However, because of Robertson's leadership role during and after the start-up of the mill, and considering the fact that he was notably responsible for the success of the pulp and paper factory for the next half century, the following brief sketch of his early life and later professional accomplishments is offered.

The blue-eyed baby boy that was born on June 11, 1879 to Cynthia and Charles Dumbreck Robertson in Cinncinnati, Ohio was named Reuben Buck. Reuben grew up to be a tall young man and attended Walnut Hills High School and then Yale University. At both scholastic levels, he ably demonstrated his physical and athletic skills on the gridiron and by heaving shot and hammers in track and field events. The caption for a school annual photo described the "nice-looking young man" as having a "winning smile which lights up his face like an electric light." After graduating from the Cincinnati Law School, he was admitted to the bar in 1901, at which time he joined his father's Cincinnati law firm, Robertson and Buchwalter.

A chance encounter on an ocean cruise changed the trajectory of Reuben Buck's life forever. It was on that voyage that he became acquainted with the son of a highly successful businessman from Hamilton, Ohio, a town located approximately twenty miles north of Cincinnati. Peter G. Thomson, Sr. was the wealthy industrialist's name and he happened to be President of the Champion Coated Paper Company in Hamilton. Following the cruise, Reuben paid a providential visit to his new friend's home, where he met the father, Peter Thomson, and a sister, Hope. This chance introduction to the lovely Hope eventually flowered into a romance, leading to an exchange of wedding vows between Hope and Reuben on June 7, 1905.[136]

The next year, Reuben was coerced to travel down to western North Carolina in his father-in-law's stead to help secure rights-of-way for a critical little railroad. The Pigeon River Railway's road was desperately needed to access the immense timber resources owned by Peter Thomson and located on the Pigeon River headlands. At that time, Thomson's giant pulp mill known as the Champion Fibre Company was under construction at Canton, North Carolina, and would soon need the valuable pulpwood. Robertson spent several months assisting an attorney named George H. Smathers, riding up and down the Pigeon River and its West Fork tributary negotiating right-of-way agreements with local farmers to build a railroad across their lands. These first

Reuben B. Robertson's college photo reflects the disposition that reportedly "won him many friends who will be willing to try to keep him out of jail, in spite of his future profession, the law." (from Canton Area Historical Museum)

dealings with the head-strong and clannish Haywood County mountaineers surely must have been an illuminating experience for him.

In the fall of 1907, at the onset of an economic crisis often referred to as the Banker's Panic, Robertson was again persuaded to go down to Canton where Thomson's new pulp mill was in the final throes of construction. His father-in-law was ill, and the family urged Reuben to go to Canton and coordinate difficult matters with the Champion Fibre Company's feuding executives. These bosses were apparently in constant dispute, and with the dire financial situation that then existed, someone needed to get the construction work out of the ditch and finished. Reuben B. often joked that he was asked to come down on a fifty-day assignment and it ended up being a fifty-year assignment. He never relinquished his leadership role at the Champion Fibre Company.

Start-up of Peter Thomson's new pulp mill and extract plant began in early 1908, and while the mill supervisors and employees struggled to get the facility running at design capacity, Robertson managed to keep the creditors off the doorstep. By mid-year, the mill had overcome the start-up inertia and moved into a profitable production situation. And as incredulous as it might seem, by that time Thomson had persuaded his son-in-law and daughter to stay awhile at Canton, and manage things for him at the mill.

Upon reflection much later, Hope Robertson remembered that they lived for a time at the rugged logging village of Sunburst, sixteen miles or so from Canton on the wild

headwaters of the Pigeon River. She distinctly recalled Reuben driving her and the children there in a wagon from Canton, and having to ford the river ten times along the way. "Part of the road was made of logs. That was where it was low and swampy. Where it was dirt, it was bumpy in the dry weather and muddy in wet weather. You'd mire up to the hubs and the oxen would have to pull you out."

She also recalled her hectic lifestyle in the woods, "I really didn't have time to get homesick. There was so much to do. I made all of my own clothes and clothes for the babies. Coming here made me learn to do everything. You had to do for yourself or do without." And just like her husband, Hope Robertson would spend the rest of her life in western North Carolina's mountains with "wonderful people," as she described the mountaineers. "Reuben and I loved the people from the start, and they loved us."[137]

Reuben B. Robertson was named General Manager of the Champion Fibre Company in 1913. Four years later he was elected vice president, and in 1925 became President and General Manager of the company. His leadership provided a list of firsts for the Canton Mill: first in the South to produce white spruce pulp by the sulphite process, the first to produce white pulp from chestnut wood, and the first company in the world to make high-quality white pulp from southern pine trees.

Although not a forester by training, Mr. Robertson was quick to recognize that the exploding pulp and paper industry in the United States, particularly in the South, demanded a perpetual and dependable supply of pulpwood. He envisioned the necessity that the current practice of "mining" forests must immediately evolve into one of "farming" forests. While others lagged behind and waited and watched, he instituted forestry conservation practices throughout the company's vast land holdings. Champion soon became a leader in farming the forests in order to provide an everlasting supply of pulpwood for manufacturing pulp and paper.

The Champion Fibre Company in Canton and the Champion Coated Paper Company in Hamilton, Ohio merged in 1935—four years after Peter G. Thomson, Sr. had passed on. The name given to the new concern was the Champion Paper and Fibre Company, and Reuben B. Robertson, Sr. was named the executive vice president. Eleven years later, in 1946, Robertson became President of the company upon the death of Peter Thomson's son, Logan G. Thomson. Then in 1950, he was elected Chairman of the Board of Directors and his son, Reuben B. Robertson, Jr., was elected president.

Throughout a long and distinguished career, Reuben B. Robertson, Sr. always treated his employees with respect and generosity. Under his leadership, the Canton mill was the first pulp mill to organize a safety committee, the first to establish a credit union, the first to establish an old-age bonus, the first to have a wage-incentive plan, and the first to establish profit sharing. Called a "quiet philanthropist," he contributed generously to the Champion and Robertson Memorial YMCA's, the Canton Public Library, several area churches, organized charities such as the Salvation Army,

A portrait of Reuben B. Robertson, Sr. as presented in Champion's monthly magazine The Log in 1951. (from Canton Area Historical Museum)

and to colleges, among other things.

Honors rained down upon Reuben B. Robertson, Sr. during his career, especially in the waning years. The *Dixie Magazine* named him Man of the South in 1950. He received the American Forestry Association's Distinguished Services Award in 1953, and the following year picked up the Conservation Award of the American Forestry Association. Other honors in 1957 included the Distinguished Citizens Award from the North Carolina Citizens Association, as well as the Human Relations Award from the National Society for the

Advancement of Management. Actually, these awards were just a sampling of the many he garnered in recognition of his great contributions to industry, humanity, and the advancement of his fellow men.

There were also many demands for his time outside of the pulp and paper mills. Filling speaking engagements and leadership positions in a multitude of civic, national, state, church, and business organizations occupied huge chunks of his busy schedule. These responsibilities included

Reuben B. Robertson, Sr. is shown in this photo with his devoted wife, Hope. (from Canton Area Historical Museum)

membership on the National War Labor Board during World War II, presidency of the American Pulp and Paper Association in 1947, director of the Wachovia Bank and Trust Company, chairman of the board of trustees for Western Carolina Teachers College and Western Carolina University, and a trustee of the University of North Carolina and Asheville School.

For a long time, Mr. Robertson lived in Asheville, North Carolina, and it was there that Hope, his wife of more than sixty years, passed away in 1958. To their credit, they had enjoyed a happy and fruitful home life while raising the following children: Mrs. Russell Norburn—the former Hope Robertson, Reuben B. Robertson, Jr., Laura Thomson Robertson (died in early childhood), and Dr. Logan Thomson Robertson.

Late in his life, Robertson told an interviewer that he had no bad habits—and never had—except for taking a rare drink ever now and then. He always identified himself with the mountains of North Carolina, and for sure no man who ever lived there touched as many lives as he did. When Robertson's life finally came to an end in 1972, Canton and western North Carolina were much better places for his having lived and worked there. A ballad in his honor, written and sung by the late Jimmy Haney of Canton, claimed that Reuben B. Robertson, Sr. walked tall in the mountains and was a legend in his own time. Undoubtedly, most men and women acquainted with Robertson would heartily concur with Haney's lyrics.[138, 139]

Endnotes

[1] *Vol. II, Reuben Robertson Memoirs* (unpublished), "Foreword."

[2] *Vol. II, Reuben Robertson Memoirs* (unpublished); p.1 of undecipherable chapter name at beginning.

[3] *Memoirs of George Smathers* (unpublished); p. 11.

[4] *Memoirs of George Smathers* (unpublished); p. 6.

[5] *Memoirs of George Smathers* (unpublished), pp. 70, 12.

[6] Corydon Bell, *A History of Champion Papers*, p. 27 (1963).

[7] *Memoirs of George Smathers* (unpublished), pp. 12, 13, 14.

[8] Thomas Crary, from New York, W. Chandler Young, and others organized the Haywood Lumber & Mining Company in 1900, as recorded in *Ancestors and Descendants of Calvert Crary and His Wife Eliza Hill*, Liberty, New York, p. 179.

[9] Newspaper clipping in possession of Doug Trimmler (possibly from the *Asheville Citizen-Times*, Asheville, N.C.) reporting on Champion YMCA dedication in about 1920.

[10] *The Evening Republican*, Columbus, Ind. (Sept, 21, 1907).

[11] *Memoirs of George Smathers* (unpublished), pp. 32, 33.

[12] *Asheville Citizen-Times*, Asheville, N.C. (Jan. 06, 1906).

[13] *The Wilmington Morning Star*, Wilmington, N.C. (Nov. 24, 1907).

[14] *Memoirs of George Smathers* (unpublished), pp. 34, 35.

[15] *News and Observer*, Raleigh, N.C. (Oct. 12, 1905).

[16] *Charlotte Observer*, Charlotte, N.C. (Sept. 21, 1905).

[17] *Asheville Citizen-Times*, Asheville, N.C. (March 11 and March 12, 1906).

[18] *News and Observer*, Raleigh, N.C. (March 12, 1906).

[19] Survey by W.H. Hargrove; Canton Area Historical Museum.

[20] Newspaper clipping (possibly the *Asheville Citizen-Times*, Asheville, N.C.) reporting on Champion YMCA dedication in April, 1920.

[21] *Memoirs of George Smathers* (unpublished), p. 55.

[22] *Asheville Citizen-Times*, Asheville, N.C. (Jan. 30, 1906).

[23] *Vol. II, Reuben Robertson Memoirs* (unpublished), pp. 2, 3 of "Sulphite & Soda."

[24] *Richmond Times Dispatch*, Richmond, Va. (Nov. 6, 1905).

[25] Corydon Bell, *A History of Champion Papers*, p. 35 (1963). Another source—*Canton: The Architecture of Our Home Town* by Camille Wells—indicates that the company's general offices were located in the former C.T. Wells house.

[26] *The North Carolinian*, Raleigh, N.C. (Oct. 12, 1905).

[27] *Engineering News-Record*, Vol. 58 (July 4, 1907).

28 *Wall Street Journal*, New York, N.Y. (March 7, 1906).

29 *Cincinnati Enquirer*, Cincinnati, Ohio (Feb. 06, 1905).

30 *Vol. II, Reuben Robertson Memoirs* (unpublished), p.1 of "Some International Incidents."

31 Beal v. Fibre Co., https://casetext.com/case/beal-v- fiber-co.

32 *Manufacturer's Record*, "North Carolina's Great Wood Pulp Plant," pp. 45–48 (Jan. 9, 1908).

33 Per the 1910 Federal Census, John N. Shoolbred was a native of England and came to the U.S. to work on the railroads in 1882.

34 *Asheville Citizen-Times*, Asheville, N.C. (March 11, 1906).

35 *Asheville Citizen-Times*, Asheville, N.C. (April 3, 1906).

36 *Asheville Citizen-Times*, Asheville, N.C. (May 11, 1906).

37 *Vol. II, Reuben Robertson Memoirs* (unpublished), pp. 2, 3 of "Some International Incidents."

38 *Manufacturer's Record*, "North Carolina's Great Wood Pulp Plant," pp. 45–48 (Jan. 9, 1908).

39 *Manufacturer's Record*, "North Carolina's Great Wood Pulp Plant," pp. 45–48 (Jan. 9, 1908).

40 *The Franklin Press*, Franklin, N.C. (Nov. 07, 1906).

41 *Asheville Citizen-Times*, Asheville, N.C. (March 28, 1906).

42 *Asheville Citizen-Times*, Asheville, N.C. (Nov. 4, 1907).

43 *Vol. II, Reuben Robertson Memoirs* (unpublished), p. 2 of "Some International Incidents."

44 Forks of Pigeon was the name given to the settlement that developed along the river bottoms surrounding the place where the east and west forks of the Pigeon River converged. In the nineteenth century Colonel Joseph Cathey established a grist mill and a general store there. The Cathey store hosted a U.S. Post Office with the address of "Forks of Pigeon," from which the community took its name. Today this area is referred to as "Bethel."

45 *Memoirs of George Smathers* (unpublished), p. 16.

46 *Asheville Citizen-Times*, Asheville, N.C. (Feb. 18, 1906).

47 It is plausible that George Smathers got Wiley Henson's war story wrong. Actual service records of the 25th N.C. Infantry Regiment, Company F (the Haywood Highlanders) indicate that a Wiley Henson from Bethel deserted from the Confederate Army in February, 1864. This date is prior to Union General U.S. Grant's siege of Petersburg and the subsequent trench warfare conducted there.

48 *Memoirs of George Smathers* (unpublished), pp. 55–69.

49 *Charlotte Observer*, Charlotte, N.C. (Nov. 12, 1906).

50 *If Rails Could Talk: Vol. 2, Sunburst and Champion Fibre*, pp. 10–13.

51 *Cincinnati Enquirer*, Cincinnati, Ohio (Sept. 12, 1906).

52 *Vol. II, Reuben Robertson Memoirs* (unpublished), pp. 1–3 of "Three Captains."

53 *Memoirs of George Smathers* (unpublished), pp. 93–98.

54 *Charlotte Observer*, Charlotte, N.C. (March 15, 1907).

55 *Charlotte Observer*, Charlotte, N.C. (March 15, 1907).

[56] *Asheville Citizen-Times*, Asheville, N.C. (Dec. 13, 1905).

[57] *U.S. Dept. of Agriculture: Bulletin No. 620, Effect of varying Certain Cooking Conditions in the Production of Sulphite Pulp from Spruce*; pp. 4–7 (March 14, 1918).

[58] *A Weekly Technical Journal for Paper and Pulp Mills*, Vol. 19, p. 56 (Oct. 4, 1916).

[59] U.S. Patent No. 762,139 (June 7, 1904).

[60] *Carolina Mountaineer Centennial* (1916), "The Champion Fibre Company of Canton."

[61] *Charlotte Observer*, Charlotte, N.C. (Nov. 10, 1907).

[62] *Electric World, Vol. XLIX*, no. 8, p. 406 (Feb. 23, 1907.

[63] *The Iron Age, Vol. LXXXIII*, January–June 1909, pp. 724–727 (March 4, 1909).

[64] *Manufacturer's Record*, "North Carolina's Great Wood Pulp Plant," pp. 45–48 (Jan. 9, 1908).

[65] *Manufacturer's Record*, "North Carolina's Great Wood Pulp Plant," pp. 45–48 (Jan. 9, 1908).

[66] *Vol. II, Reuben Robertson Memoirs* (unpublished), p. 2 of "Some International Incidents."

[67] *Manufacturer's Record*, "North Carolina's Great Wood Pulp Plant," pp. 45–48 (Jan. 9, 1908).

[68] *Manufacturer's Record*, "North Carolina's Great Wood Pulp Plant," pp. 45–48 (Jan. 9, 1908).

[69] *Manufacturer's Record*, pp. 45–48 (Jan. 9, 1908).

[70] *Manufacturer's Record*, pp. 45–48 (Jan. 9, 1908).

[71] *Roxboro Courier*, Roxboro, N.C. (Jan. 02, 1907).

[72] *Vol. II, Reuben Robertson Memoirs* (unpublished), p. 3 of "Some International Incidents."

[73] *Manufacturer's Record*, pp. 45–48 (Jan. 9, 1908).

[74] *Vol. II, Reuben Robertson Memoirs* (unpublished), pp. 1,2 of "Some International Incidents."

[75] *Charlotte Observer*, Charlotte, N.C. (Nov. 10, 1907).

[76] *Manufacturer's Record*, pp. 45–48 (Jan. 9, 1908).

[77] Camille Wells, "Furness, Thomas (1882–1976)," http://ncarchitects.lib.ncsu.edu/people/P000510 (2010).

[78] *Asheville Citizen-Times*, Asheville, N.C. (Aug. 15, 1906).

[79] *Manufacturer's Record*, pp. 45–48 (Jan. 9, 1908).

[80] *Cincinnati Enquirer*, Cincinnati, Ohio (Dec. 10, 1906).

[81] Charlotte Observer, Charlotte, N.C. (April 17, 1907).

[82] *Asheville Citizen-Times*, Asheville, N.C. (Aug. 3, 1907).

[83] The so-called "Jincie Patton" tract was named after the unmarried sister of James McConnell Patton. Jincie (or Jincy) Patton inherited sixty acres of land from her father, James Patton (1780–1854), and this land was to be hers "so long as she remained single." Jincie never married and died in 1892. The source of this information is the National Register of Historical Places Inventory form for the Patton Farm, dated October, 1974. The Patton Farm was, and still is, located in Haywood County on the old Clyde Road between Canton and Clyde, N.C.

[84] *Memoirs of George Smathers* (unpublished), pp. 42–50.

[85] *Memoirs of George Smathers* (unpublished), pp. 29–31.

[86] *Carolina Mountaineer Centennial* (1916), "Canton's Champion Fibre Cabinet."

[87] *Asheville Citizen-Times*, Asheville, N.C. (Aug. 03, 1907).

[88] *Wall Street Journal*, New York, N.Y. (June 19, 1906).

[89] *News and Observer*, Raleigh, N.C. (June 25, 1907).

[90] *Charlotte Observer*, Charlotte, N.C. (July 23, 1907).

[91] *Memoirs of George Smathers* (unpublished), pp. 81–91.

[92] *The Wilmington Messenger*, Wilmington, N.C. (May 26, 1907).

[93] *Charlotte Observer*, Charlotte, N.C. (July 06, 1907).

[94] *Roxboro Courier*, Roxboro, N.C. (Jan. 02, 1907).

[95] *Greensboro Daily News*, Greensboro, N.C. (March 14,1907).

[96] *Charlotte Observer*, Charlotte, N.C. (March 03, 1907).

[97] *Charlotte Observer*, Charlotte, N.C. (March 16, 1907).

[98] *News and Observer*, Raleigh, N.C. (March 17, 1907).

[99] *News and Observer*, Raleigh, N.C. (March 23, 1907).

[100] Beal v. Fibre Co., https://casetext.com/case/beal-v-fiber-co.

[101] *Asheville Citizen-Times*, Asheville, N.C. (June 26, 1907).

[102] *Asheville Citizen-Times*, Asheville, N.C. (Aug. 25, 1907).

[103] *Asheville Citizen-Times*, Asheville, N.C. (Sept. 01, 1907).

[104] *Asheville Citizen-Times*, Asheville, N.C. (Sept. 03, 1907).

[105] *Vol. II, Reuben Robertson Memoirs* (unpublished), pp. 3,4, "Three Captains."

[106] *News and Observer*, Raleigh, N.C. (May 22, 1907).

[107] *Asheville Citizen-Times*, Asheville, N.C. (June 26, 1907).

[108] *Charlotte Observer*, Charlotte, N.C. (Sept. 15, 1907).

[109] *Asheville Citizen-Times*, Asheville, N.C. (Sept. 12, 1907).

[110] *Memoirs of George Smathers* (unpublished), p. 100.

[111] *If Rails Could Talk: Vol. 2*, Sunburst and Champion Fibre, p. 12.

[112] *Charlotte Observer*, Charlotte, N.C. (Nov. 08, 1907).

[113] *Asheville Citizen-Times*, Asheville, N.C. (Nov. 23, 1907).

[114] *Vol. II, Reuben Robertson Memoirs* (unpublished), pp. 1–4, "A Letter of Marque."

[115] Pulp Mill Foundation Plan by George F. Hardy, obtained from Evergreen Packaging (Canton Mill). *Charlotte Observer*, Charlotte, N.C. (Nov. 10, 1907).

[116] *Charlotte Observer*, Charlotte, N.C. (Nov. 10, 1907).

[117] The automatic sprinkler system was installed by the General Fire Extinguisher Co. of Charlotte, N.C., according to the *Charlotte Observer*, Charlotte, N.C. (Oct. 9, 1907).

[118] *Asheville Citizen-Times*, Asheville, N.C. (Jan. 21, 1908).

[119] *Charlotte Observer*, Charlotte, N.C. (Oct. 30, 1907).

[120] *Vol. II, Reuben Robertson Memoirs* (unpublished), pp. 5,6, "Three Captains."

[121] *Greensboro Patriot*, Greensboro, N.C. (July 29, 1908).

[122] *Vol. II, Reuben Robertson Memoirs* (unpublished), pp. 1–5, "Sulphite & Soda."

[123] Elwood R. Maunder, *An Oral History Interview with Reuben B. Robertson & E.L. Demmon* (Feb. 15, 1959).

[124] *Charlotte Observer*, Charlotte, N.C. (June 23, 1907).

[125] *If Rails Could Talk: Vol. 1*, Crestmont and Champion Fibre, pp. 20–37.

[126] *Asheville Gazette-News*, Asheville, N.C. (April 1, 1911).

[127] *Corydon Bell*, A History of Champion Papers, p. 35 (1963).

[128] Camille Wells, *Canton: The Architecture of Our Home Town*, Canton Historical Commission (1985), pp.245–246.

[129] Elwood R. Maunder, *An Oral History Interview with Reuben B. Robertson & E.L. Demmon* (Feb. 15, 1959).

[130] Allen Roudebush, *Review of Robertson Archives*, Ramsey Library, Asheville, N.C., "Peter Gibson Thomson" (May, 1990).

[131] "The Champion Coated Paper Company," Laurel Court: The Home of Peter G. Thomson, www.laurelcourt.com/champion-paper- company.

[132] *The Log*, "Peter G. Thomson, pp. 5–14 (Oct., 1928).

[133] Corydon Bell, "A History of Champion Papers" (1963).

[134] *Memoirs of George Smathers* (unpublished), p. 109.

[135] Robert J. Buck, *Trail Blazers of the Thomson Gamble Family* (1948).

[136] Oral interview with Peter G. Thomson, Sr.'s Great-Grandson Peter G. Robinson (Oct. 20, 2017).

[137] *Asheville Citizen-Times*, Asheville, N.C. (Jan. 18, 1991).

[138] *Asheville Citizen-Times*, Asheville, N.C. (Dec. 27, 1972).

[139] *Haywood Enterprise*, Waynesville, N.C. (Dec. 28, 1972).

Bibliography

Books

Jones, Carroll C. *Rooted Deep in the Pigeon Valley: A Harvest of Western North Carolina Memories.* Wilmington, North Carolina. Winoca Press, 2009.

Sullivan, Ronald C. and Ledford, Gerald. *If Rails Could Talk: Logging in the North Carolina Great Smoky Mountains, Volume 1, Crestmont & Champion Fibre.* (privately-published, 2016).

Sullivan, Ronald C. and Ledford, Gerald. *If Rails Could Talk: Logging in the North Carolina Great Balsams, Volume 2, Sunburst & Champion Fibre.* (privately-published, 2017).

Wells, Camille. *Canton: The Architecture of Our Home Town.* Canton Historical Commission, 1985.

Special Collections

Canton Area Historical Museum's extensive collection of archives and artifacts related to the Champion Fibre Company and the Champion Paper and Fibre Company.

Robertson, Reuben B., Sr. *Memoirs of Reuben Robertson, Sr., Volume II* (unpublished manuscript edited by Allen Roudebush). Canton Area Historical Museum.

Roudebush, Allen. *Review of Robertson Archives, Ramsey Library, University of North Carolina at Asheville, North Carolina.* May, 1990. (unpublished).

Smathers, George H. *Memoirs of Geo. Smathers* (unpublished manuscript edited by Allen Roudebush). Canton Area Historical Museum.

Newspapers and Magazines

Asheville Citizen-Times. Asheville, North Carolina.
Asheville Gazette-News. Asheville, North Carolina.
A Weekly Technical Journal for Paper and Pulp Mills, Vol. 19, Oct. 4, 1916.
Carolina Mountaineer Centennial (1916). Waynesville, North Carolina.
Charlotte Observer. Charlotte, North Carolina.
Cincinnati, Enquirer. Cincinnati, Ohio.
Electric World. New York, New York. McGraw Publishing Company, Feb. 23, 1907.
Engineering News Record, Vol. 58. New York, New York, July 4, 1907.
Greensboro Daily News. Greensboro, North Carolina.
Greensboro Patriot. Greensboro, North Carolina.
Haywood Enterprise. Waynesville, North Carolina.

Manufacturer's Record, Vol. 52. Baltimore, Maryland, January 9, 1908.

News and Observer. Raleigh, North Carolina.

Newspaper clipping in possession of Doug Trimmler (possibly from the *Asheville Citizen-Times*, Asheville, N.C.) related to the Champion YMCA dedication in April, 1920.

Richmond Times Dispatch. Richmond, Virginia.

Roxboro Courier. Roxboro, North Carolina.

The Evening Republican. Columbus, Indiana.

The Franklin Press. Franklin, North Carolina.

The Iron Age, Vol. LXXXIII, New York, New York. David Williams Company, March 4, 1909.

The North Carolinian. Raleigh, North Carolina.

The Wilmington Messenger. Wilmington, North Carolina.

The Wilmington Morning Star. Wilmington, North Carolina.

Wall Street Journal. New York, New York.

Other

A Weekly Technical Journal for Paper and Pulp Mills, Vol. 19, Oct. 4, 1916.

Bell, Cordyn. *A History of Champion Papers*. 1963. (unpublished).

Buck, Robert J. *Trail Blazers of the Thomson-Gamble Family*. Privately printed in Asheville, 1948.

Crary, Jerry. *Ancestors and Descendants of Calvert Crary and His Wife Eliza Hill, Liberty, New York*. New York, 1917.

Hardy, George F. Engineering drawing of the original pulp mill foundations. Copy obtained from Evergreen Packaging (Canton Mill).

Maunder, Elwood R. *An Oral History Interview with Reuben B. Robertson & E.L. Demmon*, February 15, 1959.

Oral interview with Patsy and Dan Kelly. August, 2017.

Oral interview with Peter G. Robinson (great-grandson of Peter G. Thomson, Sr.). October 20, 2017.

The Log of the Champion Family (volumes held in Canton Area Historical Museum). Champion Fibre Company and Champion Paper and Fibre Company.

U.S. Dept. of Agriculture: Bulletin No. 620. "Effect of Varying Certain Cooking Conditions in the Production of Sulphite Pulp from Spruce," March 14, 1918.

W.H. Hargrove and Shoolbred Survey. Reproduced in edited format in *If Rails Could Talk, Volume 1* (p. 76) *and Volume 2* (p. 34), (the original borrowed from Canton Area Historical Museum has not been found).

Index

V

variable-speed machinery, 41, 132

W

W.J. Oliver Company, 35

water pollution, 73–75

Waynesville Band, 93

Waynesville, North Carolina, 3–4, 8–9, 23,
    30–31, 33, 41, 74, 77, 133

Wells, Charles T., 10, 77, 78

West Fork of the Pigeon River, 4, 7–8, 29,
    30–31, 35, 152

William Whitmer & Sons, 135

wood preparation buildings, 41, 89, 107,
    110, 115, 125, 135

Y

Yandle Brothers, 35, 93, 95–97, 133

Yandle Brothers safety record, 96–97

ABOUT THE AUTHOR

Carroll C. Jones was born and raised in the mountains of Haywood County, North Carolina, in the small paper-mill town of Canton. He is a direct descendant of the Hargrove, Cathey, Shook, and Moore families who pioneered the Forks of Pigeon region of Haywood County (present-day Bethel, N.C.), the setting for most of his books. After attending the University of South Carolina in Columbia, where he played football for the USC Gamecocks and earned a degree in civil engineering, he began an extended career in the paper industry lasting more than three decades. Carroll's professional work led him out of the Carolina highlands to Brazil, South America and then back to the U.S. In the late 1980's and early 1990's, he managed the Canton Modernization Project which brought Champion International Paper Company's Canton mill into compliance with the EPA's environmental water and air standards. After that, he moved to Pensacola, Florida and worked in various mill and corporate management positions for Champion and International Paper. Now retired and living in Morristown, Tennessee, he juggles retreats to the N.C. mountains and fly fishing with his love for writing. To his credit Carroll now has six award-winning books: *The 25th North Carolina Troops in the Civil War, Rooted Deep in the Pigeon Valley, Captain Lenoir's Diary, Master of the East Fork, Rebel Rousers* (winner of the prestigious 2016 President's Award from the North Carolina Society of Historians), and *August's Treasure*. You can find out more about Carroll and his books on his website at http://carrolljones.weebly.com.

Printed in the USA
CPSIA information can be obtained
at www.ICGtesting.com
LVHW070744090923
757435LV00042B/436